MW00639369

FIELD GUIDE TO
CRAYFISHES
OF THE MIDWEST

CHRISTOPHER A. TAYLOR
GUENTER A. SCHUSTER
DANIEL B. WYLIE

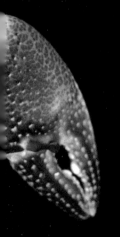

ILLINOIS NATURAL HISTORY SURVEY
MANUAL 15

Prairie Research Institute
Brian Anderson, Interim Executive Director

Illinois Natural History Survey
Geoff Levin, Interim Director
1816 South Oak Street
Champaign, Illinois 61820

Editors: Charles E. Warwick, Jeff M. Levengood, and Danielle M. Ruffatto

Photos by authors unless otherwise credited.

ISBN: 1-882932-37-4

P1112287-0.6M-03-2015

Library of Congress Control Number: 2015934556

Citation: Taylor, C.A., G.A. Schuster, and D.B. Wylie. 2015. Field Guide to Crayfishes of the Midwest. Manual 15. Illinois Natural History Survey, Champaign. x + 145 pp.

TABLE OF CONTENTS

ACKNOWLEDGMENTS

Numerous individuals assisted with our preparation of this field guide. Of primary importance are the many individuals who, over many years, assisted with the field collection of specimens. Given that the careers of the authors span several decades, there are far too many individuals to remember and name here. We can only say a collective thank you to everyone who has spent any amount of time in the field with us.

Roger Thoma provided valuable information on the status of crayfishes in Ohio and we are thankful for that input. For assistance with museum visits, we are grateful to B. Sietman of the Minnesota Department of Natural Resources and A. Simons at the Bell Museum of Natural History, University of Minnesota.

For assistance with graphics we are grateful for the efforts of D. Ruffatto. We also thank the tireless efforts Illinois Natural History Survey editors D. Ruffatto and C. Warwick for their help with page layout and editing.

Funding for printing costs was provided by the Illinois Natural History Survey Publications Committee and we graciously thank them for their support. The authors would also like to thank their wives and families for putting up with the many long absences from home over the years while they were out chasing crayfishes.

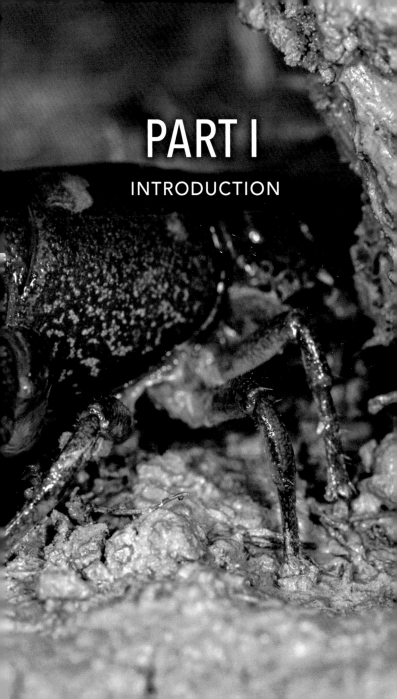

PART I

INTRODUCTION

INTRODUCTION

Crayfishes, also known as crawfishes, crawdads, or mudbugs, are recognizable by almost anyone who has spent time in and around lakes or creeks in the midwestern United States. They are a diverse and ecologically important component of freshwater aquatic and semi-aquatic ecosystems and are native to every continent except Africa and Antarctica. Crayfishes can be found in almost every type of aquatic and semi-aquatic habitat and, in many of those habitat types, can represent the largest and most abundant type of invertebrate present.

This field guide is intended to provide users with all of the information needed to identify all currently known species of shrimps and crayfishes found in the midwestern states of Minnesota, Wisconsin, Iowa, Illinois, Missouri (north of the Missouri River), Indiana, Ohio, and Michigan. Distribution maps, illustrations, photos, and a dichotomous identification key are provided to assist the user in reaching this goal. Additional information on habitat, biology, and conservation status of each species is also provided in the species accounts.

DIVERSITY AND DISTRIBUTION OF CRAYFISHES

Crayfishes are members of the Phylum Arthropoda, the largest group of named organisms with over 1 million members. The phylum includes insects, spiders, and crustaceans. They are characterized by possessing hard exoskeletons that are continuously shed or molted and re-grown. Within Arthropoda, crayfishes belong to the Order Decapoda, which also includes both freshwater and marine shrimps, crabs, and lobsters. Approximately 620 species of crayfishes are currently recognized worldwide and they are found mostly in termperate regions of every continent except Africa and Antarctica. Crayfishes, however, have been introduced into Africa.

Crayfishes found in North America belong to one of two families, Astacidae or Cambaridae. The males in both families possess long modified structures for sperm transfer called gonopods or first pleopods. In Cambaridae, the gonopods change shape as the male alternates between reproductively active (form I) and reproductively inactive (form II) stages while in Astacidae the gonopods' shape does not change. The Astacidae is a small family composed of approximately 13 species and is distributed in Europe, western Asia, the extreme northwestern United States, and southwestern Canada. Only five species are known to occur in the United States, all of which occur west of the Continental Divide. With over 410 species, the family Cambaridae contains over two-thirds of the world's crayfish species, 90% of which occur in the eastern United States, primarily in the southeast.

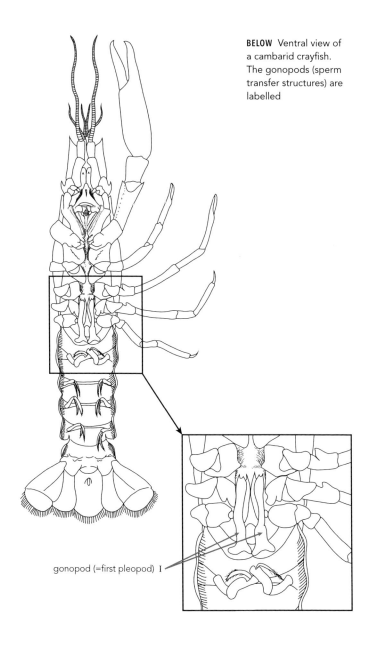

BELOW Ventral view of a cambarid crayfish. The gonopods (sperm transfer structures) are labelled

gonopod (=first pleopod) I

ABOVE *Cambarus diogenes* (Devil Crayfish), a midwestern crayfish species

RIGHT Composite of nine midwestern crayfish species

While not as diverse as crayfishes in the south-eastern United States, those in the the Midwest, as defined for this book as Minnesota, Wisconsin, Iowa, Illinois, Missouri (north of the Missouri River), Indiana, Ohio, and Michigan, comprise a relatively rich crayfish fauna. The region is home to 39 species and more may be discovered and described in the future. The fauna is dominated by the genus *Orconectes* (22 species), while the genera *Cambarus* (10 species), *Procambarus* (4 species), *Cambarellus* (2 species), and *Fallicambarus* (1 species) are also present.

BIOLOGY OF CRAYFISHES

Midwestern crayfishes occupy a wide range of habitats. They occur in rivers, creeks, swamps, sloughs, subterranean creeks, springs, ephemeral ponds, reservoirs, ditches, and wet fields. Relative to other aquatic groups such as fishes, turtles, or even mussels, the life-history of most midwestern crayfish species is poorly documented. However, in general, the life-histories of midwestern species follow one of two patterns, that of a burrower or that of a non-burrower. With these factors in mind, most of the behavior, growth, reproduction, longevity, and foraging behavior information presented below represents a summation of generalized life-history data gathered from burrowing and non-burrowing species found across North America.

BURROWING The primary life-history trait of crayfishes that determines the habitats in which they can live is their propensity for burrowing. All crayfishes will burrow, however, some spend their entire life constructing burrows while others will burrow only when the need arises. Crayfishes respire with gills and therefore require an aquatic habitat. Crayfishes may also briefly get oxygen from the air, but to extract it, their gills must

LEFT Burden Branch Creek in southern Illinois. Photo by Michael R. Jeffords

BELOW Morphology of crayfish burrows. (a) that of a primary burrowing species; (b, c, d) those of a secondary burrowing species; and (e) that of a tertiary burrowing species. From Hobbs (1981)

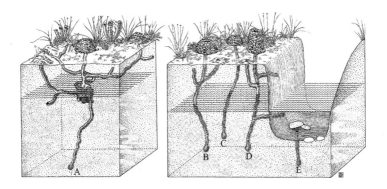

remain moist and the atmosphere must have nearly 100% relative humidity. Those species that spend most of their life burrowing will usually dig vertically into the substrate to reach the water table, thus allowing them to colonize habitats with semi-permanent standing water such as low lying ditches, shallow ponds, wet fields and prairies, or to survive times of drought in more permanent aquatic habitats.

PRIMARY BURROWERS are those species that excavate elaborate burrows, spending almost their entire lives in them. These burrows can be up to 3 m in depth and be composed of multiple chambers, tunnels, and surface openings. Primary burrowers will emerge from their burrows to forage for food or look for mates during wet spring or fall months and on warm humid nights.

SECONDARY BURROWERS are those species that spend a significant portion of their lives in burrows, usually adjacent to creeks and ponds, and will frequent them throughout the year. The burrows of secondary burrowers are usually less complex than those of primary burrowers and differ from them in that they usually have a connection or tunnel leading to a permanent water body.

TERTIARY BURROWERS are sometimes referred to as non-burrowers and are those species that only occasionally retreat into simple and shallow vertical burrows during times of drought or low water levels. Tertiary burrowers usually inhabit permanent flowing rivers and creeks.

As crayfish excavate their burrows, they will push the loose soil or mud up and out of the burrow opening. This activity will usually lead to the formation of a chimney rising several centimeters above the ground. Chimneys of secondary burrowers can be frequently seen lining creek and river margins while those of primary burrowers can be found in open pastures, low lying ditches, ephemeral ponds, and even plowed agricultural fields. Burrowing crayfishes are also known to plug the openings of their burrows with mud during dry or cold conditions and remain inactive for weeks or even months.

LIFE CYCLE, GROWTH, AND REPRODUCTION   Because crayfishes have a hardened exoskeleton that prevents growth, the process of molting plays a significant role in the life history of a crayfish. The lives of crayfishes consist of a continuous process of shedding, or molting, their old exoskeleton,

and growing and hardening the new exoskeleton. This allows the body to grow in the interim. In the days leading up to molting, crayfishes begin to breakdown the calcium salts in their exoskeleton and store a small amount of them in small whitish disklike structures called gastroliths. Gastroliths are found in the stomachs of crayfishes and provide the important initial source of calcium used to harden the new exoskeleton. Crayfishes in the molting process are very vulnerable to predation because they are soft and unable to move effectively. During this time, they will usually find refuge under rocks, in woody debris, or in burrows.

Crayfishes begin life as fertilized eggs attached to the underside of the female's abdomen. In the Midwest, females are usually found with eggs attached to their abdomens from early March to early June. These females are referred to as being ovigerous or "in berry" and will carry their eggs for several days to several weeks. After hatching from the egg, juvenile crayfishes will stay attached to the underside of the female's abdomen for several days, usually going through two or three molts as body size increases. After detaching from the female, juvenile crayfishes begin life as free-living individuals foraging for food, finding shelter, and growing to adult size.

LEFT Ovigerous or "in berry" female crayfish

ABOVE Juvenile crayfishes attached to female's abdomen. Photo by Jennifer Mui

RIGHT Reproductively
active "form I" female
with swollen, creamy
white glair glands

Growth is most rapid in the first summer of life; crayfishes can molt as many as 14 times during this period and triple or quadruple in body size. As food becomes less abundant and water temperatures decline during the winter months, growth and molting will typically cease. Adults of most species will usually molt only twice each year during the remainder of their lives, once in the spring and then again in the fall.

All midwestern crayfishes have males that exhibit a cycle of dimorphism associated with reproduction. Males are classified as either form I or form II. Form I males are reproductively active and differ from form II males in having longer, more pointed terminal elements of the gonopod and larger hooks on the ischia of the pereiopods. The tips of the terminal elements of the gonopod have a yellowish, translucent appearance. Usually in the late spring and early summer and again in the fall, form I males will molt into the reproductively inactive form II stage. Males of most species can reach sexual maturity (form I) in their first year of life. Female crayfishes may also alternate between reproductively active and inactive states (Wetzel 2002). Reproductively active "form I" females are usually found in fall and spring months and differ from form II females in having wider abdominal segments and swollen glair glands (described below).

Copulation in midwestern crayfishes occurs mostly in the fall months from September to November. Sperm is transferred to the female via the male's gonopods. The sperm is inserted into a storage chamber called the annulus ventralis located between the last two pairs of pereiopods of the female where it is stored overwinter. In the late winter or early spring months (usually February or March), females will move to a secluded location and will release their unfertilized eggs from openings at the bases of their third pair of pereiopods. They will simultaneously release the sperm stored in their annulus ventralis, thereby

fertilizing the eggs. Prior to egg laying, the pleopods are coated with a sticky substance, known as glair, excreted from glands on the underside of the abdomen. The fertilized eggs are moved to the underside of her abdomen where they become attached to the pleopods. Females carrying eggs will protect them by curling their tail fans under their abdomens. The total number of eggs fertilized and carried by a female is dependent on species and the body size of the female; larger females generally carry more eggs. The number of eggs found on a female can range from less than 50 to 400. Some crayfish species may also copulate in early spring months with

BELOW Annulus ventralis of a female *Cambarus bartonii cavatus* (Appalachian Brook Crayfish)

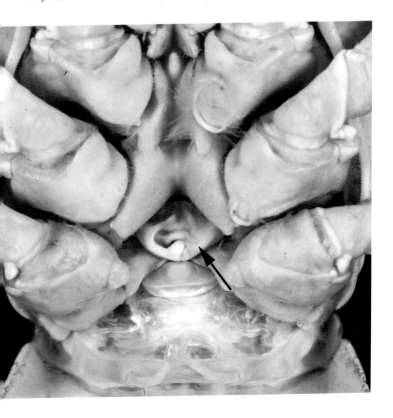

females using the sperm to fertilize eggs later that same spring. In more southern latitudes of North America, copulation commonly occurs in the spring with eggs being extruded in the fall.

Copulation is usually initiated by the male after coming in contact with a female. There is some courtship behavior, which can initially appear to be hostile, that results in species and sex recognition. This initially starts with antennal flicking, followed by the male grabbing the female with his chelae. She eventually capitulates and allows the male to turn her onto her back. Once this is done, he will crawl on top of her and hold her chelae and pereiopods with his chelae. At this point, she is completely subdued, and the pair becomes locked together as the male fits the hooks on the ischia of his pereiopods into corresponding depressions on the underside of the female. The copulating pair can remain locked together for an extended period of time, often an hour or more, during which the male will transfer sperm via his gonopods into the female's annulus ventralis.

ABOVE Crayfish copulation. Photo by Chris Lukhaup

LONGEVITY It is estimated that most midwestern crayfishes live from two to three years. In general, species that grow to larger sizes such as *Cambarus diogenes* and *Orconectes virilis* may live for five or six years while smaller species, such as those in the genus *Cambarellus*, may live only one year.

DIET Historically treated as opportunistic omnivores, crayfishes have been shown to eat a variety of food items, both living and dead. These include aquatic and terrestrial vegetation, plant detritus, insects, snails, other aquatic crustaceans, and even fish. Some evidence has suggested that crayfishes are primarily carnivores, but in the absence of animal material, they become facultative omnivores and scavengers (Momot 1995). Crayfishes play an important role in ecosystem function by consuming detritus and vegetation and converting that material into animal protein. That protein is then made available to a wide range of other aquatic and terrestrial organisms such as insects, fishes, birds, and mammals. Butler et al. (2003) reported that over 240 different species of animals are known to feed on crayfishes. Crayfishes are also known to occasionally consume carrion and assist with its breakdown in aquatic ecosystems.

LEFT From top to bottom: *Cambarus diogenes*, *Orconectes virilis*, *Cambarellus puer*, and *Cambarellus shufeldtii*

COLLECTION AND CONSERVATION OF CRAYFISHES

COLLECTION OF CRAYFISHES Crayfishes can easily be collected from, and sometimes observed in, their habitats. Given the variation in habitats in which they occur, a variety of methods needs to be used. A nylon minnow seine with no larger than 3–4 mm mesh and measuring approximately 3.1 m in length and 1.2 m in depth can be used effectively in a variety of habitats. The seine should have small lead weights along the bottom edge and be attached between brail poles. Seines are most effective in shallow riffles and pools of creeks and in lakes and ponds lacking lush growths of aquatic vegetation. In riffles, the seine should be set perpendicular to the current with the lead line firmly held against the bottom. The substrate immediately upstream of the seine should then be vigorously disturbed by kicking and/or turning over rocks by hand. Pools of creeks or ponds can be seined by rapidly pulling the seine through the water, being careful to keep the lead line against the bottom. In ponds or pools with abundant submergent vegetation, hand-held dip-nets often prove to be more effective. An alternative method of collecting crayfishes in pools and ponds is with traps. Numerous trap designs are available; however, those similar to a funnel minnow trap made with wire or hard plastic mesh with an opening at the end of the funnel are the most effective. Traps may or may not be baited. If baited, cat food or any type of animal flesh or tissue such as beef liver can be used and left submerged for one to several days. Trapping usually captures the largest individuals at a location and their presence in traps may prevent other individuals of other species from entering the traps.

Burrowing crayfishes present a different situation for collecting. While some adult and juvenile individuals can be collected in standing water with a

ABOVE Seining for crayfishes

minnow seine, their presence in standing water is highly seasonal and usually occurs only in the spring months. Extracting crayfishes from their burrows can be a time-consuming venture. The most successful method is to use hand shovels or trowels to physically enlarge the opening and dig out the burrow. Crayfishes will often retreat to the deepest chamber or tunnel of the burrow complex as one begins to excavate the burrow and the collector will usually need to dig to the end of the burrow or deep enough to stick their hand into the deepest part. As many burrows in a colony can be unoccupied, it is best to look for and dig out those burrows with signs of fresh mud that has been pushed out of the burrow opening. If the water table of a burrow is only a few inches below the surface, one can enlarge the opening by hand and agitate the water. If the collector remains quiet and is patient, he or she can be rewarded by a crayfish coming to the water's surface to investigate the disturbance. The crayfish's presence will usually be given away as it waves it antennae near the water's surface. The collector must then quickly pin the crayfish against the burrow wall and extract it. Adult burrowing crayfishes will sometimes come out of their burrows or sit at the burrow openings on warm and humid or rainy nights. Individuals wandering away from their burrows can be collected by hand using a flashlight. Those sitting at the entrace can be enticed to leave their burrows by carefully placing a worm on a hook at the end of fishing line direcly in front of the individual and slowly moving it away from the crayfish.

CONSERVATION OF CRAYFISHES Crayfishes are one of the most threatened groups of aquatic organisms found in North America, with slightly less than half of all species in need of conservation attention (Taylor et al. 2007). Crayfish are susceptible to the same threats facing other aquatic organisms, mainly habitat loss/alteration and the introduction of non-native species. However, the high level of imperilment in crayfishes is due mainly to the narrow native ranges of many species. The

RIGHT Crayfish chimney with signs of fresh mud. Photo by Jennifer Mui

BELOW *Cambarellus* species. Photo by Jennifer Mui

ABOVE *Orconectes rusticus* (Rusty Crayfish), a non-native, invasive crayfish species in many regions of the United States

limited ranges can magnify the impacts of habitat alteration and the introduction of harmful non-native species. Habitat alteration can take many forms, but for crayfishes, creek channelization with the removal of rocky substrates or woody debris, wetland drainage, or the impoundment of flowing streams can drastically affect the total population size of some species.

The introduction of non-native crayfishes is the greatest threat to native crayfish populations. When introduced into new areas, whether continents, countries, or drainages within the same state, non-native crayfishes often rapidly increase in population size and they can aggressively displace native species. There are several examples in the United States of native species being totally eliminated from lakes or stretches of rivers after a non-native species was introduced (Lodge et al. 2000). Vigilance must be exercised by individuals who come in contact with live crayfishes to prevent the spread of non-native species. This would include educators who use live crayfishes for laboratory teaching, aquarium hobbyists, and

fisherman who use them for bait. Under no circumstances should any crayfish be released into waters from which they were not collected.

Taylor et al. (2007) listed one midwestern crayfish species as threatened (*Orconectes inermis testii*) and one as vulnerable (*O. stannardi*). However these listings, and others such as those from the International Union for the Conseveration of Nature (IUCN), do not afford species legal projection from direct taking or destruction of habitat. True protection from such activities is afforded to species listed at the state or federal levels as either Endangered or Threatened under their respective Endangered Species Acts (ESAs). Currently, no midwestern crayfish are protected under the federal ESA, but several species are listed by state ESAs. Those listings are noted in the Status sections of their respective species account pages in this field guide.

ABOVE *Orconectes lancifer* (Shrimp Crayfish), a state endangered species in Illinois

HOW TO USE THIS BOOK

The primary goal for this field guide is to assist biologists, interested naturalists, and educators in identifying midwestern crayfishes. To meet that end, we include a dichotomous identification key and individual species accounts for all 39 crayfish species known to occur in the Midwest. We have tried to keep the amount of technical terminology to a minimum, but in many cases there are not alternative terms for morphological features used in the identification of crayfishes. Terms used in the identification key and species accounts are illustrated at the beginning of the *Midwest Crayfish Identification Key* section (page 32) and defined in the *Glossary* (page 138).

IDENTIFICATION OF SPECIMENS The use of the dichotomous key in this field guide is the most accurate method for identifying crayfish. However, the key is based on morphological characters found on form I males (see *Biology of Crayfishes*, page 9, and pages 32–33). As such, the user is required to examine either a live or dead form I male under a dissecting microscope or with a hand lens and progressively move through the couplets of the key. After arriving at a species name, the user should then turn to the page indicated and confirm that the distributional data and illustrations presented for that species match the specimen and location from which it was collected. Alternatively, if a form I male is unavailable, the user may be able to infer the specimens' identification by studying the color plates and illustrations of nonform I characters of species known to occur in the region from which the specimen was collected. In many cases across the Midwest, only four or fewer species may be known from a particular geographic region. It should be noted that due to their constant cycle of molting, the intensity of colors shown by crayfishes can be highly variable. Freshly molted individuals have much brighter colors, especially reds and blues, than individuals that have not molted in several weeks or months. These older intermolt individuals can also be covered with thin layers of dark brown or black stained debris. Because of this variation, the user should be cautious in arriving at an identification of a specimen based solely on color.

Another cautionary note pertains to the claws (chelae) of crayfishes. Several crayfish species, particularily in the genus *Cambarus*, are diagnosed using chelae morphology. Crayfishes can regenerate chelae that are lost and since these regenerated chelae differ in size, shape, and tubercle pattern from original (nonregenerated chelae), only original chelae should be used for identification purposes. Regenerated chelae will usually be longer and thinner than original chelae and will have tubercles of equal size along the opposable margins of the fingers of the chelae.

BELOW From top to bottom: original chelae and regenerated chelae

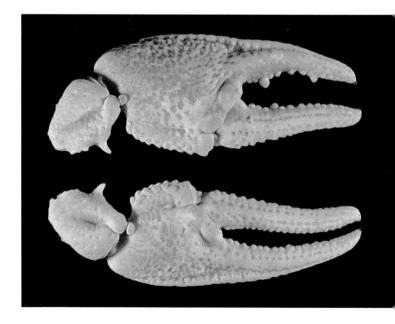

DISTRIBUTION & STATUS Known from lower Mississippi and Ohio river drainages in a band extending from southern Illinois northeast through southern Michigan and western Ohio. Widespread and common in appropriate habitats across its range.

PAINTEDHAND MUDBUG
Cambarus polychromatus Thoma, Jezerinac, and Simon 2005

KEY CHARACTERS
1. Closed areola
2. Spoon-shaped rostrum without marginal spines
3. Two short, sharply angled and sickle-shaped terminal elements on form I gonopod

SIMILAR SPECIES
- Devil Crayfish [*Cambarus diogenes*]
- Little Brown Mudbug [*C. thomai*]
- Prairie Crayfish [*Procambarus gracilis*]
- Digger Crayfish [*Fallicambarus fodiens*]

DESCRIPTION Rostrum deeply excavated; margins converge terminally and terminate in small rounded tubercles or smoothly merge with base of short acumen. Chela large and robust, fingers short; dorsal surface of palm covered with many small rounded tubercles. Areola closed or linear. Form I male gonopod with two short elements curved about 90 degrees to main axis of gonopod, tip of central projection blunt. Life colors olive green to dark brown, larger knobs on chela bright orange to red; bright orange to red posterior stripe on each abdominal segment; tips of fingers red to orange.

Differs from the Devil Crayfish by having numerous small round tubercles on dorsal surface of palm of chela; Little Brown Mudbug in lateral view by the distinctly downward curved rostrum and having strong offsetting orange coloration in life; Prairie Crayfish by having two terminal elements on the gonopod; Digger Crayfish by having a suborbital angle on edge of the carapace.

HABITAT Considered a primary or secondary burrower. Primary burrows usually found in low lying open fields. Commonly found in secondary burrows directly associated with low-lying, open water habitats such a streams or ponds. Young of the year and adults may be found in open water in early spring.

SPECIES TREATMENTS Each species treatment contains three components: (1) color photographs of whole animals and individual body parts (A, chela; B, mesial view of form I gonopod; C, mesial view of form II gonopod; D, rostrum) for each species; (2) text describing aspects of each species' anatomy; and (3) a range map.

LEFT Sample species treatment with dorsal view of whole animal and individual body parts (A, chela; B, mesial view of form I gonopod; C, mesial view of form II gonopod; D, rostrum)

A   B   C   D

Common and scientific names used in the species accounts were taken from Taylor et al. (2007) or, if described since 2007, from the original peer-reviewed description for that species. The authority and year of description of each species is also given.

The *Key Characters* section lists several morphological features of the species that will help initially distinquish it from other similar midwestern species. The *Similar Species* section lists other crayfish species found in the Midwest that would most likely be confused with the species under consideration based on size, coloration, body shape, or male gonopod shape. The *Description* section provides an estimate of the average size for the species and describes morphological features such as the shape of the rostrum, chelae, areola, carapace, and form I male gonopods. While color can be somewhat variable in crayfish, we also list the most common color and pattern found in the species. How the species in question differs from those crayfish listed in the *Similar Species* section is described. The *Distribution and Status* section describes the species' range in the region of the Midwest covered by this field guide. This range should not be interpreted as its total known range as, in a few cases, the species in question occurs in other adjacent regions of the United States. Notes on the spread of species that have been introduced into other areas of the Midwest are also given. It can be assumed that the ranges of those introduced species may change over time as new populations are recorded. It also provides a general assessment of the species' range-wide population status and if it is recognized as protected in any midwestern states (see *Collection and Conservation of Crayfishes*, page 20). Finally, the *Habitat* section lists those general habitats in which the species will most likely be encountered.

ADDITIONAL INFORMATION More detailed life history and distributional information for midwestern crayfish species can be found in the following state-specific works, listed in the *Literature Cited* section (page 140) and below.

Illinois: Page (1985)
Indiana: Thoma and Armitage (2008)
Michigan: Creaser (1931)
Minnesota: Helgen (1990)
Missouri: Pflieger (1996)
Ohio: Thoma and Jezerinac (2000)
Wisconsin: Hobbs and Jass (1988)

CRAYFISHES AND SHRIMPS OF THE MIDWEST IDENTIFICATION KEY

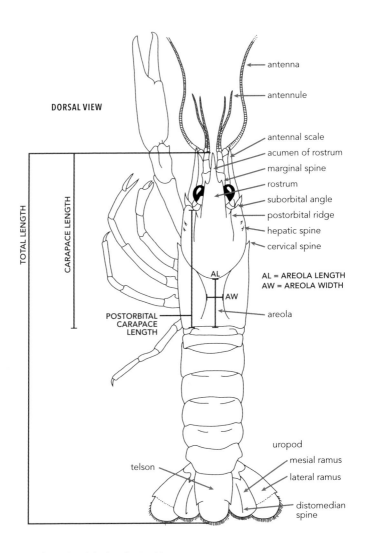

DORSAL VIEW

antenna

antennule

antennal scale

acumen of rostrum

marginal spine

rostrum

suborbital angle

postorbital ridge

hepatic spine

cervical spine

TOTAL LENGTH

CARAPACE LENGTH

AL

AW

AL = AREOLA LENGTH
AW = AREOLA WIDTH

POSTORBITAL
CARAPACE
LENGTH

areola

uropod

mesial ramus

telson

lateral ramus

distomedian
spine

The use of this dichotomous key is the most accurate method for identifying crayfish and shrimp species found in the Midwest. In most cases, the key used morphological features found on form I males.

LEFT & BELOW
Morphological structures of cambarid crayfish. Modified from Hobbs (1981)

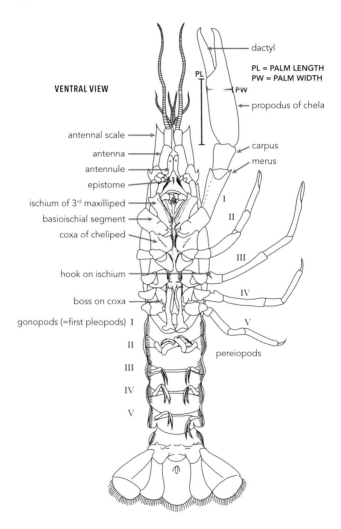

VENTRAL VIEW

dactyl

PL = PALM LENGTH
PW = PALM WIDTH

PL

PW

propodus of chela

antennal scale

antenna

antennule

epistome

ischium of 3rd maxilliped

basioischial segment

coxa of cheliped

hook on ischium

boss on coxa

gonopods (=first pleopods) I

II

III

IV

V

carpus

merus

I

II

III

IV

V

pereiopods

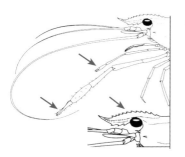

1A First two pairs of legs with chelae, teeth along top edge of rostrum, shrimplike body with abdomen laterally compressed–Shrimps **2**

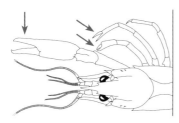

1B First three pairs of legs with chelae, no teeth along top edge of rostrum, abdomen dorsoventrally flattened–Crayfishes..................... **3**

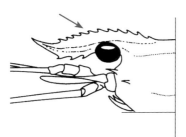

2A 9–13 teeth along upper edge of rostrum.............. Ohio River Shrimp (*Macrobrachium ohione*)

Found only in Mississippi and Ohio rivers bordering southern Illinois, Indiana and Ohio–species is not addressed in this Field Guide.

2B 6–8 teeth along upper edge of rostrum............. Mississippi Grass Shrimp (*Palaemonetes kadiakensis*)

Found across Mississippi and lower Ohio river drainges–species is not addressed in this Field Guide.

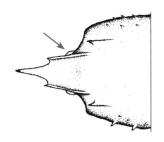

3A Body lacking pigment, white in color; eyestalks present but pigmented eyes absent .... **p. 92**

Ghost/Unarmed Crayfish
(*Orconectes inermis inermis*
and *O. inermis testii*)

3B Body with pigment, colors variable, including tan, green, brown, red and cream, with or without dark stripes on tips of finger and carapace; with pigmented eyes.... **4**

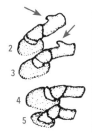

4A Males with hooks on ischia of second and third pereiopods (first and second walking legs); adult size small, never exceeding 40 mm total length.................................... **5**

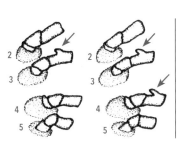

4B Males with hooks on ischia of third or third and fourth pereiopods (second or second and third walking legs), never with hooks on second pereiopod; adult size exceeding 40 mm total length...... **6**

5A Terminal elements of form I male gonopods curved.......................**p. 58**

Swamp Dwarf Crayfish
(Cambarellus puer)

5B Terminal elements of male gonopods straight....................**p. 60**

Cajun Dwarf Crayfish
(Cambarellus shufeldtii)

6A Areola obliterated or linear...........7

6B Areola open, space very narrow to wide... 13

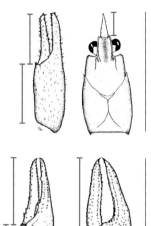

7A Fingers of chelae short, length of dactyl less than length of palm; acumen very long, its length equal to or greater than twice the width of rostrum at marginal spines .... **p. 98**

Shrimp Crayfish
(*Orconectes lancifer*)

7B Fingers of chelae longer, length of dactyl greater than length of palm, acumen significantly shorter than width of rostrum............................ **8**

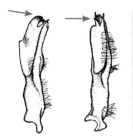

8A Gonopod of male sickle shaped, with two short, laterally flattened and wide elements curved at approximately 90 degrees **9**

8B Gonopods of male with more than two elements, elements straight or slightly curved, elements frequently obscured by setae **12**

9A Suborbital angle absent...........**p. 82**

Digger Crayfish
(Fallicambarus fodiens)

9B Suborbital angle present.............**10**

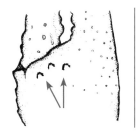

10A Dactyl length greater than 1.8 times palm length; one or more subpalmar tubercles present ....
....**p. 66**

Devil Crayfish
(Cambarus diogenes)

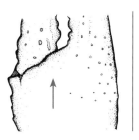

10B Dactyl length less than 1.8 times palm length; zero or one subpalmar tubercles present **11**

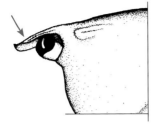

11A Top edge of rostrum straight in lateral view, although somewhat angled downward .... **p. 80**

Little Brown Mudbug
(*Cambarus thomai*)

11B Top edge of rostrum rounded downward in lateral view .... **p. 70**

Paintedhand Mudbug
(*Cambarus polychromatus*)

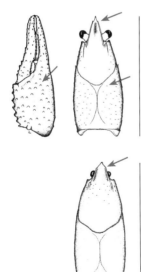

12A Sides of body and top of chelae covered with small tubercles; rostrum strongly tapering with small marginal spines; live adult individuals usually red in color ....
.... **p. 130**

Red Swamp Crawfish
(*Procambarus clarkii*)

12B Sides of body and top of chelae lacking small tubercles; rostrum moderately tapering with smoothly rounded or angular margins; live adult individuals usually brown in color .... **p. 132**

Prairie Crayfish
(*Procambarus gracilis*)

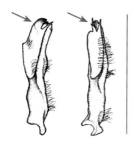

13A Gonopod of male with more than two short terminal elements, elements frequently obscured by setae.. **14**

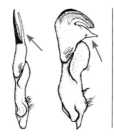

13B Gonopod of male with two terminal elements, not obscured by setae, elements may take several forms (short and straight, short and curved, long and thin).....
.... **15**

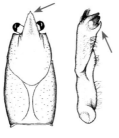

14A Rostrum with small marginal spines; terminal elements of gonopod strongly curved; large adults with sides of body and top of chelae covered with small tubercles................................. **p. 128**

White River Crawfish
(Procambarus acutus)

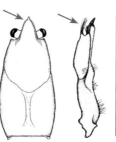

14B Rostrum without small marginal spines, margins smoothly merge into base of acumen; terminal elements of gonopod straight or weakly curved .... **p. 134**

Vernal Crayfish
(Procambarus viaeviridis)

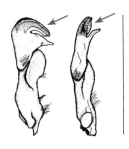

15A Gonopod of male with two short and curved elements; cephalic to caudal width of central projection at its base close to 2 times its length, central projection more laterally flattened and wide **16**

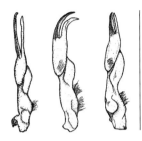

15B Gonopod of male with two thin elements, cephalic to caudal width of central projection at its base greater than 3 times its length, central projection not strongly laterally flattened; elements either curved or straight........................ **25**

16A Gonopod of male with short elements curved distinctly less than 90 degrees **17**

16B Gonopod of male with elements curved at approximately 90 degrees or more **18**

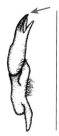

17A Central projection of gonopod of male tapering to a thin tip ..... **p. 120**

Sloan Crayfish
(*Orconectes sloanii*)

17B Central projection of gonopod of male not tapering to thin tip, tip truncated................................... **p. 96**

Kentucky Crayfish
(*Orconectes kentuckiensis*)

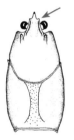

18A Rostral margins concave and terminating in marginal spines........
.... **p. 74**

Depression Crayfish
(*Cambarus rusticiformis*)

18B Rostral margins not concave and not terminating in spines or tubercles, usually smoothly rounded.. **19**

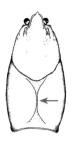

19A Areola open but very narrow, usually with room for no more than one punctuation across its narrowest part.........................**p. 68**

Ortmann's Mudbug
(Cambarus ortmanni)

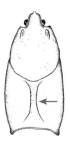

19B Areola open and not narrow, with space for two or more punctations across its narrowest part.............**20**

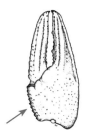

20A Palm region of chelae with two rows of tubercles.........................**21**

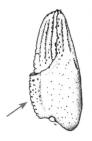

20B Palm region of chelae with a single row of tubercles **23**

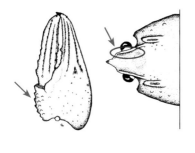

21A Row of tubercles along mesial margin of palm with 7 or fewer tubercles; rostral margins greatly thickened and truncated.......... **p. 76**

Teays River Crayfish
(Cambarus sciotensis)

21B Row of tubercles along mesial margin of palm with 8 or more tubercles; rostral margins not greatly thickened, margins gradually merging into base of acumen.. **22**

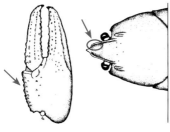

22A Dorsoventral depression at base of fixed finger of chela, outside edge of chela appears "pinched" when viewed from side; areola short, less than 40% of carapace length ....
.... **p. 72**

Big Water Crayfish
(Cambarus robustus)

22B No dorsoventral depression at base of fixed finger of chela, outside edge of chela not "pinched"; areola long, greater than 40% of carapace length ....
.... **p. 78**

Cavespring Crayfish
(Cambarus tenebrosus)

23A Rostral margins thickened and truncated.....................................**24**

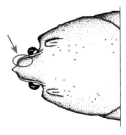

23B Rostral margins not thickened, margins gradually merging into base of acumen........................**p. 62**

Appalachian Brook Crayfish
(*Cambarus bartonii cavatus*)

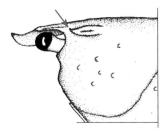

24A Postorbital ridges terminate in tubercle or sharp spine ....**p. 76**

Teays River Crayfish
(*Cambarus sciotensis*)

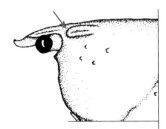

24B Postorbital ridges do not terminate in tubercle or sharp spine, instead being broadly rounded ....**p. 64**

Rock Crawfish
(*Cambarus carinirostris*)

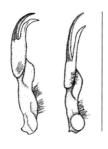

25A Both terminal elements of gonopod curved, curve away from body when gonopod is lying in its normal position between bases of walking legs **26**

25B At least one terminal element of gonopod straight and in line with main axis of gonopod or both elements divergent **28**

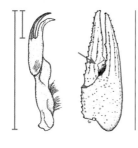

26A Central projection of gonopod short, length less than 1/3 total length of gonopod; dactyl with deep incision at its base........... **p. 88**

Calico Crayfish
(*Orconectes immunis*)

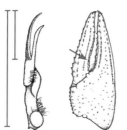

26B Central projection of gonopod long, length greater than 1/3 total length of gonopod; dactyl lacking deep incision at its base.............. **27**

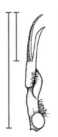

27A Central projection of gonopod 45% or less than total length of gonopod; chelae usually with dark flecks scattered across dorsal surface; abdomen usually with paired dark blotches on each segment..... **p. 126**

Virile Crayfish
(*Orconectes virilis*)

27B Central projection of gonopod greater than 45% of total length of gonopod; chelae without dark flecks on dorsal surfaces and with dark spot at base of moveable finger; abdomen lacking paired dark blotches.. **p. 110**

Spothanded Crayfish
(*Orconectes punctimanus*)

28A Terminal elements of gonopod short and strongly divergent and V-shaped .... **p. 90**

Indiana Crayfish
(*Orconectes indianensis*)

28B Terminal elements of gonopod not strongly divergent....................... **29**

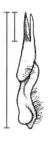

29A Central projection of gonopod 30% or less of total length of gonopod; if close to 30% (28-31%) strong shoulder usually present at base of central projection **30**

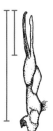

29B Central projection of gonopod greater than 31% total length of gonopod **34**

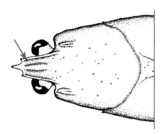

30A Median carina present on middle of dorsal surface of rostrum........ **31**

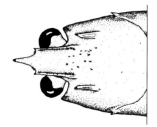

30B Dorsal surface of rostrum lacking median carina.............................. **32**

31A Mesial process of male gonopod with caudal spur .... **p. 122**

Little Wabash Crayfish
(*Orconectes stannardi*)

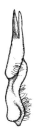

31B Mesial process of male gonopod lacking caudal spur .... **p. 108**

Northern Clearwater Crayfish
(*Orconectes propinquus*)

32A Strong shoulder at base of central projection of gonopod........... **p. 102**

Allegheny Crayfish
(*Orconectes obscurus*)

32B No strong shoulder at base of central projection **33**

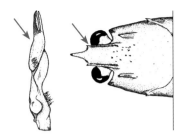

33A Rostral margins straight and parallel; cephalic edge of pleopod slightly curved .... **p. 118**

Sanborn's Crayfish
(*Orconectes sanbornii*)

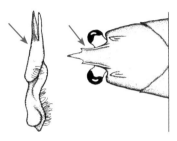

33B Margins of rostrum converging anteriorly, rostrum significantly narrower at marginal spines than at its base; cephalic edge of pleopod straight .... **p. 86**

Shawnee Crayfish
(*Orconectes illinoiensis*)

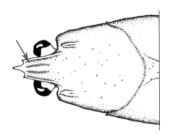

34A Median carina present on middle of dorsal surface of rostrum 35

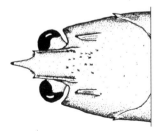

34B Dorsal surface of rostrum lacking median carina 39

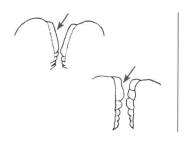

35A Incisor region of at least one mandible with straight edge....... **37**

35B Incisor region of both mandibles not straight, with distinct teeth... **36**

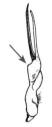

36A Angular shoulder present at base of central projection of gonopod; fingers shorter, moveable finger two times or less than length of mesial margin of palm.............. **p. 84**

Spiny Stream Crayfish
(*Orconectes cristavarius*)

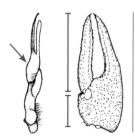

36B Weakly rounded or no shoulder present at base of central projection of gonopod; fingers long, moveable finger greater than two times length of mesial margin of palm .... **p. 106**

Bigclaw Crayfish
(*Orconectes placidus*)

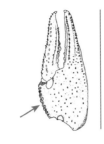

37A Tubercles on palm restricted to two well-defined rows............ **p. 100**

Golden Crayfish
(Orconectes luteus)

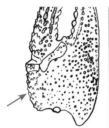

37B Tubercles on palm not restricted to two well-defined rows................. **38**

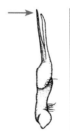

38A Central projection of pleopod straight (Lost River drainage in southcentral IN)...................... **p. 124**

Sinkhole Crayfish
(Orconectes theaphionensis)

38B Central projection of pleopod with curved tip (southcentral OH)...........
.... **p. 114**

Norwood River Crayfish
(Orconectes raymondi)

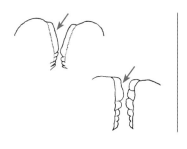

39A Incisor region of at least one mandible with straight edge....... **40**

39B Incisor region of both mandibles not straight, with distinct teeth... **42**

40A Pleopod with long terminal elements, elements more than 44% of total length of pleopod (extreme southern IN).............. **p. 94**

Kentucky River Crayfish
(*Orconectes juvenilis*)

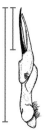

40B Pleopod with shorter terminal elements, elements less than 44% of total length of pleopod **41**

41A Shoulder on gonopod large and sharply pointed; in life posterio-lateral surface of carapace with large rust-colored spot; central projection of pleopod usually less than 40% of total pleopod length .. .. **p. 116**

Rusty Crayfish
(Orconectes rusticus)

41B Shoulder on gonopod small and not sharply pointed; posterio-lateral surfaces of carapace lacking large rust-colored spot; central projection of pleopod usually greater than 40% of total pleopod length .... **p. 100**

Golden Crayfish
(Orconectes luteus)

42A Central projection of pleopod very long, 50% or more of total pleopod length .... **p. 112**

Phallic Crayfish
(Orconectes putnami)

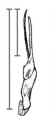

42B Central projection less than 50% of total pleopod length.................. **43**

43A Ventral surface of carpus with distomedian spine; in life dorsal surface of carapace usually with two dark saddles .... **p. 106**

Bigclaw Crayfish
(*Orconectes placidus*)

43B Ventral surface of carpus without distomedian spine; in life dorsal surfaces of body and chelae usually covered with dark spots .... **p. 104**

Leopard Crayfish
(*Orconectes pardalotus*)

PART II
SPECIES TREATMENTS

DISTRIBUTION & STATUS Found only in Mississippi and Ohio river drainages in extreme southern Illinois. Locally abundant in suitable habitat.

SWAMP DWARF CRAYFISH
Cambarellus puer Hobbs 1945

KEY CHARACTERS
1. Small body size
2. Three curved terminal elements on form I male gonopod
3. Hooks on the ischia of the second and third pair of walking legs

SIMILAR SPECIES
• Cajun Dwarf Crayfish [*Cambarellus shufeldtii*]

DESCRIPTION Small body size, adults rarely exceeding 28 mm total length. Rostrum flat; convex margins that converge terminally and terminate in small spines. Chela with short fingers, fingers less than length of mesial margin of palm region. Areola wide. Form I male gonopod with three terminal elements that curve at approximately 90 degrees away from the ventral surface of the crayfish when gonopod is laying in its normal position between bases of walking legs. Life colors variable, base color of carapace, abdomen, and chela ranging from rust red to light brown to gray. Two longitudinal dark brown or black stripes or rows of spots present on dorsal surface of carapace and abdomen.

Differs from Cajun Dwarf Crayfish in that elements of form I gonopod are strongly curved rather than straight.

HABITAT Cypress swamps and other permanently flooded low areas near creeks. May occasionally inhabit roadside ditches. Usually found amongst dense growths of live or decaying aquatic vegetation.

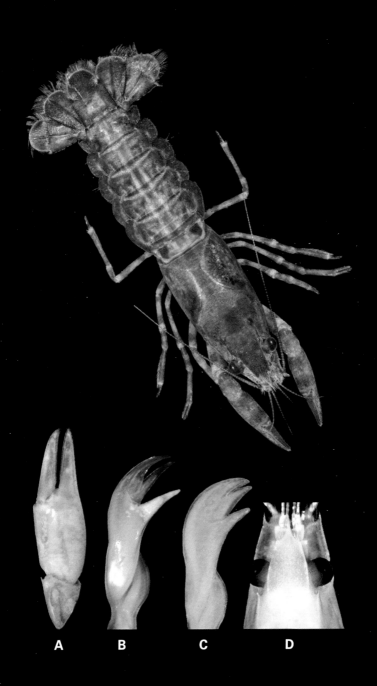

A   B   C   D

DISTRIBUTION & STATUS Found only in Mississippi and Ohio river drainages in extreme southern Illinois and a restricted portion of the Mississippi and lower Illinois river drainages north of the St. Louis region. Locally abundant in suitable habitat.

CAJUN DWARF CRAYFISH
Cambarellus shufeldtii (Faxon 1884)

KEY CHARACTERS
1. Small body size
2. Three straight terminal elements on form I male gonopod
3. Hooks on the ischia of the second and third pair of walking legs

SIMILAR SPECIES
- Swamp Dwarf Crayfish [*Cambarellus puer*]

DESCRIPTION Small body size, adults rarely exceeding 28 mm total length. Rostrum flat; margins converge terminally and terminate in small spines. Chela with short fingers, fingers less than length of mesial margin of palm region. Areola wide. Form I male gonopod with three straight terminal elements in line with the main shaft of the gonopod, tip of at least one element may be slightly curved. Life colors variable, base color of carapace, abdomen, and chela ranging from rust red to light brown to gray. Two longitudinal dark brown or black stripes or rows of spots present on dorsal surface of carapace and abdomen.

Differs from Swamp Dwarf Crayfish in having elements of form I gonopod that are straight rather than strongly curved.

HABITAT Swamps, sloughs, ditches and other sluggish flowing lowland habitat. Usually found amongst dense growths of live or decaying aquatic vegetation.

A   B   C   D

DISTRIBUTION & STATUS Widespread throughout Ohio River drainages in central Ohio and extreme eastern Indiana. Widespread and common in suitable habitat across its range.

APPALACHIAN BROOK CRAYFISH
Cambarus bartonii cavatus Hay 1902

KEY CHARACTERS
1. Rostrum broad, spoon shaped without marginal spines
2. Areola moderately wide
3. Two short, sharply angled and sickle-shaped elements on form I male gonopod

SIMILAR SPECIES
- Rock Crawfish [*Cambarus carinirostris*]
- Ortmann's Mudbug [*C. ortmanni*]
- Big Water Crayfish [*C. robustus*]
- Teays River Crayfish [*C. sciotensis*]
- Cavespring Crayfish [*C. tenebrosus*]

DESCRIPTION Well developed suborbital angle. Rostrum excavated, without a median carina; margins not thickened and gradually taper into base of acumen, acumen short. Chela large with moderately long fingers, mesial margin of palm of chela with single row of low, sometimes poorly defined tubercles. Areola moderately wide. Form I male gonopod with two elements curved about 90 degrees to main axis of gonopod. Life colors uniform across body, from golden straw to dark brown to green.

Differs from Rock and Teays River Crayfish by having thin rostral margins that are not truncated; differs from Ortmann's Mudbug by well developed suborbital angle and wider areola; differs from Big Water Crayfish in lacking a deep depression at base of fixed finger on chela; differs from Cavespring Crayfish by having a single row tubercles along the mesial margin of the palm of the chela.

HABITAT Most commonly found in smaller upland rocky streams under large, well-secured rocks in areas of little or no flow.

A   B   C   D

DISTRIBUTION & STATUS Found in Lake Erie and Ohio River drainages in extreme northeastern Ohio. Common across most of its Ohio range, however, some localized population reductions have occurred at sites impacted by mining and clear-cutting.

ROCK CRAWFISH
Cambarus carinirostris Hay 1914

KEY CHARACTERS
1. Rostrum broad, spoon shaped without marginal spines or tubercles
2. Areola moderately wide
3. Two short, sharply angled and sickle-shaped elements on form I male gonopod

SIMILAR SPECIES
- Appalachian Brook Crawfish [*Cambarus bartonii cavatus*]
- Ortmann's Mudbug [*C. ortmanni*]
- Big Water Crayfish [*C. robustus*]
- Teays River Crayfish [*C. sciotensis*]
- Cavespring Crayfish [*C. tenebrosus*]

DESCRIPTION Well-developed suborbital angle. Rostrum excavated, with weak anterior median carina; margins thickened and truncated, acumen short. Chela large with long fingers, mesial margin of palm of chela with single row of low, sometimes poorly defined tubercles. Areola moderately wide. Form I male gonopod with two elements curved about 90 degrees to main axis of gonopod. Life color uniform and varies from golden straw to dark brown.

Differs from Appalachian Brook Crawfish by having truncated rostral margins; differs from Teays River Crayfish in having broadly rounded ends of postorbital ridges; differs from Ortmann's Mudbug by having a well-developed suborbital angle and wider areola; differs from Big Water Crayfish in lacking a deep depression at base of fixed finger on chela; differs from Cavespring Crayfish by having a single row of tubercles along the mesial margin of the palm of the chela.

HABITAT Predominately occurs in small, cool-water creeks but can also be found in larger rivers. Occurs under large cobble and rocks.

DISTRIBUTION & STATUS Found in the Mississippi and Ohio river and Great Lakes drainages across the Midwest. Absent from central and eastern Ohio and extreme western Iowa and Minnesota. Widespread and common in appropriate habitats across its range.

DEVIL CRAYFISH
Cambarus diogenes Girard 1852

KEY CHARACTERS
1. Closed areola
2. Spoon-shaped rostrum without marginal spines
3. Two short, sharply angled and sickle-shaped terminal elements on form I gonopod

SIMILAR SPECIES
- Paintedhand Mudbug [*Cambarus polychromatus*]
- Little Brown Mudbug [*C. thomai*]
- Prairie Crayfish [*Procambarus gracilis*]
- Digger Crayfish [*Fallicambarus fodiens*]

DESCRIPTION Rostrum deeply excavated; margins straight, converge terminally and merge with base of short acumen. Chela large and robust, short fingers; mesial margin of palm with two rows of rounded tubercles and a third row on dorsal surface of palm. Areola closed or linear. Form I male gonopod with two short elements curved about 90 degrees to main axis of gonopod, tip of central projection tapering to an angular tip. Life colors olive green to brown, larger knobs on chela and rostral margins deep red; deep red transverse posterior stripe on each abdominal segment, tips of fingers red.

Differs from the Paintedhand and Little Brown Mudbug by having one or more small round sub-palmer tubercles; differs from Prairie Crayfish in having two terminal elements on the gonopod; differs from Digger Crayfish in having a suborbital angle on edge of the carapace.

HABITAT Considered a primary or secondary burrower. Primary burrows found in low-lying, open fields or woodlands. Commonly found in secondary burrows directly associated with low-lying, open water habitats such a streams, ponds, or lakes. Young of the year and adults may be found in open water in early spring and early summer.

A   B   C   D

DISTRIBUTION & STATUS Widespread throughout Ohio River drainage from southwestern Ohio to north-central Indiana, with one disjunct population in extreme northwestern Indiana. Common to uncommon across its range. Some evidence of range expansion in the eastern portion of its Midwest range.

ORTMANN'S MUDBUG

Cambarus ortmanni Williamson 1907

KEY CHARACTERS

1. Rostrum broad, spoon shaped, without marginal spines or tubercles
2. Areola narrowly open
3. Two short, sharply angled and sickle-shaped elements on form I male gonopod

SIMILAR SPECIES

- Appalachian Brook Crayfish [*Cambarus bartonii cavatus*]
- Rock Crawfish [*C. carinirostris*]
- Big Water Crayfish [*C. robustus*]
- Teays River Crayfish [*C. sciotensis*]
- Cavespring Crayfish [*C. tenebrosus*]

DESCRIPTION Suborbital angle absent. Rostrum excavated, without median carina; margins thickened and gradually taper into base of short acumen. Chela large, with moderately long fingers, mesial margin of palm of chela with row of low, sometimes poorly defined tubercles, second incomplete row with two to seven tubercles. Areola narrowly open. Form I male gonopod with two elements curved about 90 degrees to main axis of gonopod, mesial process longer than central projection. Life color uniform and varies from blue gray to dark brown.

Differs from Appalachian, Big Water, Teays River, Cavespring Crayfish and Rock Crawfish by having a very narrow areola.

HABITAT Considered a primary or secondary burrower. Primary burrows found in low-lying, open fields. Most populations commonly found in secondary burrows directly associated with springs, ditches, small streams, or low-lying ponds. Young of the year and adults may be found in open water in early spring and early summer.

A B C D

DISTRIBUTION & STATUS Known from lower Mississippi and Ohio river drainages in a band extending from southern Illinois northeast through southern Michigan and western Ohio. Widespread and common in appropriate habitats across its range.

PAINTEDHAND MUDBUG

Cambarus polychromatus Thoma, Jezerinac, and Simon 2005

KEY CHARACTERS

1. Closed areola
2. Spoon-shaped rostrum without marginal spines
3. Two short, sharply angled and sickle-shaped terminal elements on form I gonopod

SIMILAR SPECIES

- Devil Crayfish [*Cambarus diogenes*]
- Little Brown Mudbug [*C. thomai*]
- Prairie Crayfish [*Procambarus gracilis*]
- Digger Crayfish [*Fallicambarus fodiens*]

DESCRIPTION Rostrum deeply excavated; margins converge terminally and terminate in small rounded tubercles or smoothly merge with base of short acumen. Chela large and robust, fingers short; dorsal surface of palm covered with many small rounded tubercles. Areola closed or linear. Form I male gonopod with two short elements curved about 90 degrees to main axis of gonopod, tip of central projection blunt. Life colors olive green to dark brown, larger knobs on chela bright orange to red; bright orange to red posterior stripe on each abdominal segment; tips of fingers red to orange.

Differs from the Devil Crayfish by having numerous small round tubercles on dorsal surface of palm of chela; Little Brown Mudbug in lateral view by the distinctly downward curved rostrum and having strong offsetting orange coloration in life; Prairie Crayfish by having two terminal elements on the gonopod; Digger Crayfish by having a suborbital angle on edge of the carapace.

HABITAT Considered a primary or secondary burrower. Primary burrows usually found in low lying open fields. Commonly found in secondary burrows directly associated with low-lying, open water habitats such a streams or ponds. Young of the year and adults may be found in open water in early spring.

A   B   C   D

DISTRIBUTION & STATUS Found in the Great Lakes and Ohio River drainages from central Michigan to northern Indiana and northern and eastern Ohio. Historically known from a few isolated locations in central Illinois, but now extirpated from that state. Common in appropriate habitats across its range.

BIG WATER CRAYFISH
Cambarus robustus Girard 1852

KEY CHARACTERS
1. Open areola
2. Spoon-shaped rostrum without marginal spines
3. Two short, sharply angled, sickle-shaped terminal elements on form I gonopod

SIMILAR SPECIES
- Ortmann's Mudbug [*Cambarus ortmanni*]
- Teays River Crayfish [*C. sciotensis*]
- Cavespring Crayfish [*C. tenebrosus*]
- Rock Crawfish [*C. carinirostris*]
- Appalachian Brook Crayfish [*C. bartonii cavatus*]

DESCRIPTION Rostrum moderately excavated; margins straight, converge terminally and merge with base of short acumen. Chela large and robust, moderately long fingers, deep depression on dorsal surface at base of fixed finger, mesial margin of palm with two rows of rounded tubercles. Areola moderately wide. Form I male gonopod with two short elements curved about 90 degrees to main axis of gonopod, tip of central projection tapering to an angular tip. Life colors olive green to dark brown; pair of dark longitudinal stripes on dorsal surface of abdomen occasionally present; tips of fingers red or orange.

Differs from Ortmann's Mudbug by having a moderately wide areola; differs from Teays River Crayfish by having thin rostral margins that gradually taper into base of acumen; differs from Cavespring Crayfish in having a deep depression on dorsal surface of chela at base of fixed finger; differs from the Rock Crawfish and Appalachian Brook Crayfish by having two rows of tubercles along the mesial margin of the palm of the chela.

HABITAT Occurs in medium to large creeks and rivers. Commonly found under large rocks.

A   B   C   D

DISTRIBUTION & STATUS Only known from the Ohio River bordering southern Illinois. Given its very limited range and its occurrence in large, navigable rivers in the Midwest, the species is infrequently encountered. As such, its status in the Midwest is unknown.

DEPRESSION CRAYFISH
Cambarus rusticiformis Rhoades 1944

KEY CHARACTERS
1. Open areola
2. Two short, sharply angled and sickle-shaped terminal elements on form I gonopod
3. Rostral margins terminate in spines

SIMILAR SPECIES
None, should not be confused with any other midwestern species.

DESCRIPTION Rostrum moderately excavated; margins concave and terminate in large rounded spines, acumen moderately long. Chela large, robust, moderately long fingers, mesial margin of palm with one row of rounded tubercles. Areola wide. Form I male gonopod with two short elements curved slightly greater than 90 degrees to main axis of gonopod, tip of central projection tapering to an angular tip. Life colors golden brown to dark brown, dark dorsal saddle at posterior edge of carapace occasionally present, tips of fingers orange or cream.

Differs from all other midwestern crayfish by having two short terminal elements that curve approximately 90 degrees to main shaft of gonopod and thick rostral margins that are convex and terminate in strong tubercles at that base of a moderately long acumen.

HABITAT Occurs in large creeks to large rivers. Commonly found under large flat rocks.

A   B   C   D

DISTRIBUTION & STATUS Only known from the Scioto River drainage in central Ohio. Common in appropriate habitats in its midwestern range.

TEAYS RIVER CRAYFISH
Cambarus sciotensis Rhoades 1944

KEY CHARACTERS
1. Open areola
2. Two short, sharply angled and sickle-shaped terminal elements on form I gonopod
3. Thickened rostral margins that abruptly terminate, do not extend into base of acumen

SIMILAR SPECIES
- Appalachian Brook Crayfish [*Cambarus bartonii cavatus*]
- Rock Crawfish [*C. carinirostris*]
- Ortmann's Mudbug [*C. ortmanni*]
- Big Water Crayfish [*C. robustus*]
- Cavespring Crayfish [*C. tenebrosus*]

DESCRIPTION Rostrum moderately excavated; margins thickened, slightly concave, and abruptly terminating, no spines or tubercles present, acumen short. Chela large and robust, with long fingers, mesial margin of palm with one or two rows of rounded tubercles. Areola wide. Form I male gonopod with two short elements curved at approximately 90 degrees to main axis of gonopod, tip of central projection tapering to an angular tip. Life colors olive green to dark brown, tips of fingers orange.

Differs from Ortmann's Mudbug by having a wide areola; differs from Big Water, Appalachian Brook, and Cavespring Crayfish by having thick rostral margins that abruptly terminate and do not extend into base of acumen; differs from the Rock Crawfish in having postorbital ridges that terminate in a tubercle or spine.

HABITAT Occurs in medium to large creeks and rivers with cobble and boulder substrates. Commonly found under large flat rocks.

A   B   C   D

DISTRIBUTION & STATUS Known from the Ohio River drainage in extreme southern Illinois and a limited portion of the Wabash and Ohio river drainages from east-central Illinois across to southeastern Indiana. Also known from a very limited portion of the Ohio River drainage in extreme southwestern Ohio. Common in appropriate habitats in its midwestern range.

CAVESPRING CRAYFISH
Cambarus tenebrosus Hay 1902

KEY CHARACTERS
1. Open areola
2. Two short, sharply angled and sickle-shaped terminal elements on form I gonopod
3. Thickened rostral margins that extend into base of acumen

SIMILAR SPECIES
- Appalachian Brook Crayfish [*Cambarus bartonii cavatus*]
- Rock Crawfish [*C. carinirostris*]
- Ortmann's Mudbug [*C. ortmanni*]
- Big Water Crayfish [*C. robustus*]
- Teays River Crayfish [*C. sciotensis*]

DESCRIPTION Rostrum moderately excavated; margins thickened, straight and converging anteriorly, margins merge with base of short acumen, no spines or tubercles present. Chela large and robust, with moderately long fingers, mesial margin of palm with two rows of rounded tubercles. Areola moderately wide. Form I male gonopod with two short elements curved at approximately 90 degrees to main axis of gonopod, tip of central projection tapering to an angular tip. Life colors variable, from olive green to light red, to light brown, fingers can be dark brown or black, tips of fingers orange.

Differs from Ortmann's Mudbug by having a moderately wide areola; differs from Teays River Crayfish by having thick rostral margins that extend into the base of the acumen; differs from Big Water Crayfish by lacking a deep depression on dorsal surface of chela at base of fixed finger; differs from Appalachian Brook Crayfish and Rock Crawfish in having two rows of tubercles along mesial margin of the palm of the chela.

HABITAT Occurs in small to large creeks with gravel and cobble substrates, small spring-fed creeks, springheads, and creeks flowing out of cave openings. Also known to occur in the twilight and dark zones of caves. Commonly found under rocks or cobble of various sizes.

A   B   C   D

DISTRIBUTION & STATUS Widespread in the Lake Erie and Ohio River drainages in a wide north-south band across central Ohio. Widespread and common in appropriate habitats across its range.

LITTLE BROWN MUDBUG
Cambarus thomai Jezerinac 1993

KEY CHARACTERS
1. Closed areola
2. Two short, sharply angled and sickle-shaped elements on form I male gonopod

SIMILAR SPECIES
- Devil Crayfish [*Cambarus diogenes*]
- Paintedhand Mudbug [*C. polychromatus*]
- Digger Crayfish [*Fallicambarus fodiens*]
- Prairie Crayfish [*Procambarus gracilis*]

DESCRIPTION Strong suborbital angle present. Rostrum deeply excavated; margins straight and converging, merging gradually with base of short acumen. Chela large and robust, mesial margin of palm of chela with row of rounded tubercles and dorsal surface of palm covered with small rounded tubercles. Areola closed or linear. Form I male gonopod with two elements curved about 90 degrees to main axis of gonopod, mesial process longer than central projection. Life color uniform dark green to dark brown, tips of fingers of chela faint red or orange.

Differs from Devil Crayfish by having numerous scattered tubercles on dorsal surface of palm of chela; differs from Paintedhand Mudbug in having a straight top edge on its rostrum; differs from Prairie Crayfish in having two terminal elements on the gonopod; differs from Digger Crayfish in having a suborbital angle on edge of the carapace.

HABITAT Considered a primary or secondary burrower. Most populations found in complex burrow systems in the floodplains of streams, ditches, and swamps. Young of the year and adults may be found in open water in early spring and early summer.

A   B   C   D

DISTRIBUTION & STATUS Known from the Mississippi and Ohio river and Great Lakes drainages from southeastern Wisconsin and central Illinois to eastern Ohio and southern Michigan. Status is difficult to assess for this species due to its burrowing behavior, but there is currently no evidence of reduction in population sizes across its range.

DIGGER CRAYFISH
Fallicambarus fodiens (Cottle 1863)

KEY CHARACTERS
1. Closed areola
2. Rostrum broad, spoon-shaped, without marginal spines
3. Two short sharply angled and sickle-shaped terminal elements on form I gonopod

SIMILAR SPECIES
- Devil Crayfish [*Cambarus diogenes*]
- Paintedhand Mudbug [*C. polychromatus*]
- Little Brown Mudbug [*C. thomai*]
- Prairie Crayfish [*Procambarus gracilis*]

DESCRIPTION Rostrum moderately excavated, wide, and spoon-shaped; margins converge terminally and merge with base of short acumen, no terminal marginal spines. Chela large and wide with flattened fingers, deep incision at base of opposable margin of moveable finger, incision opposed by large tubercles at base of fixed finger. Areola closed or linear. Form I male gonopod with two short elements curved about 90 degrees to main axis of gonopod, central projection with truncated tip. Life colors light to dark brown, two faint longitudinal stripes may be present of dorsal surface of abdomen, tips of fingers red to orange.

Differs from the Devil Crayfish, Paintedhand and Little Brown Mudbug by lacking a suborbital angle on edge of the carapace; differs Prairie Crayfish in having two terminal elements on the form I gonopod and lacking strong angular tubercles on the mesial margin of the chela palm region.

HABITAT A primary burrowing species, the Digger Crayfish is found in burrows up to several feet deep. Populations are normally found in ephemeral wetlands, wooded floodplains, and low-lying fields.

A   B   C   D

DISTRIBUTION & STATUS Restricted to a few direct tributaries to the Ohio River in extreme south-central Ohio. Common in its range.

SPINY STREAM CRAYFISH
Orconectes cristavarius Taylor 2000

KEY CHARACTERS
1. Two long thin elements on form I male gonopod, both elongated and mostly straight
2. Rostrum with median carina

SIMILAR SPECIES
- Kentucky River Crayfish [*Orconectes juvenilis*]
- Golden Crayfish [*O. luteus*]
- Phallic Crayfish [*O. putnami*]
- Norwood River Crayfish [*O. raymondi*]
- Rusty Crayfish [*O. rusticus*]
- Sinkhole Crayfish [*O. theaphionensis*]

DESCRIPTION Rostrum moderately excavated, with median carina; margins almost straight, gradually converging and terminating in spines, acumen short. Chela large, with moderately long fingers, mesial margin of palm with two rows of tubercles. Areola moderately wide. Form I male gonopod with two thin elongated elements, central projection with slight curve and with angular shoulder at its base. Life colors brown to olive green, tips of fingers of chela orange, with subterminal black band, large knobs at base of moveable finger of chela yellow to bright orange, dark dorsal saddle at posterior edge of carapace.

Differs from the Kentucky River, Phallic, and Rusty Crayfish by having a median carina; differs from Norwood River and Sinkhole Crayfish by having dentate mandibles; differs from Golden Crayfish by lacking two dark dorsal saddles.

HABITAT Found in small to large creeks with gravel, cobble, or boulder substrates. Commonly found under large gravel or rocks, but can occasionally be found in woody debris or undercut banks.

A   B   C   D

DISTRIBUTION & STATUS Found only in the Mississippi and Ohio river drainages in extreme southern Illinois. Common in appropriate habitats across its range in southern Illinois.

SHAWNEE CRAYFISH
Orconectes illinoiensis Brown 1956

KEY CHARACTERS
1. Two short straight terminal elements on form I male gonopod
2. Rostrum lacking a median carina

SIMILAR SPECIES
- Indiana Crayfish [*Orconectes indianensis*]
- Allegheny Crayfish [*O. obscurus*]
- Northern Clearwater Crayfish [*O. propinquus*]
- Sanborn's Crayfish [*O. sanbornii*]
- Little Wabash Crayfish [*O. stannardi*]

DESCRIPTION Rostrum excavated; straight or nearly straight margins that converge and terminate in strong spines. Chela large with moderately long fingers, one or two rows of rounded turbercles along mesial margin of palm region. Areola wide. Form I male gonopod with two short straight elements, elements in line with main shaft and with nearly straight dorsal edge. Life colors light to dark reddish brown, tips of fingers red with black subterminal bands.

Differs from Northern Clearwater Crayfish in possessing a rostrum that lacks a carina; differs from Little Wabash Crayfish in lacking a caudal spur on mesial process of the form I gonopod; differs from Allegheny Crayfish in lacking a strong shoulder at the base of the form I gonopod elements; differs from Indiana Crayfish by having very straight terminal elements on the form I gonopod; differs from Sanborn's Crayfish by having converging rostral margins.

HABITAT Found in small- to medium-sized creeks with firm substrates of sand, gravel, or cobble. Usually found under rocks or in woody debris.

A   B   C   D

DISTRIBUTION & STATUS Found in most river drainages across the Midwest with the exception of northwestern Minnesota, central and northern Wisconsin, and southern and eastern Ohio. The species has frequently been used in the bait trade which may explain the isolated populations in Wisconsin. Other undocumented populations may exist. Widespread and common across most of the Midwest.

CALICO CRAYFISH
Orconectes immunis (Hagen 1870)

KEY CHARACTERS
1. Two thin, strongly curved terminal elements on form I male gonopod
2. Deep incision at base of movable finger of chela
3. Jagged, cream colored stripe down the dorsal surface of carapace

SIMILAR SPECIES
- Spothanded Crayfish [*Orconectes punctimanus*]
- Virile Crayfish [*O. virilis*]

DESCRIPTION Rostrum moderately excavated; margins slightly convex that terminate in small spines; spines may be very small and difficult to discern in some large specimens. Chela large with moderately long fingers, with large, forward angling tubercles along mesial margin of palm region and movable finger, deep incision at base of opposable surface of movable finger. Areola narrowly open. Form I male gonopod with two thin, moderately long, and strongly curved elements that curve away from the ventral surface of the crayfish when gonopod is laying in normal position between bases of walking legs. Life colors gray to light green, with gray or cream colored stripe of varying widths running down midline of carapace and abdomen, tips of fingers red or orange.

Differs from Virile and Spothanded Crayfish by having much shorter form I gonopod elements that curve close to 90° to main shaft of gonopod and a deep incision at base of movable finger of chela.

HABITAT Found in a wide variety of habitats including small gravel-bottomed streams, sluggish flowing mud-bottomed creeks, lakes, ponds, and well-vegetated flooded ditches. It can build simple burrows to escape desiccation in shallow ponds or ditches that may occasionally dry out.

A B C D

DISTRIBUTION & STATUS Found in lower Wabash River drainage in extreme southeastern Illinois and southwestern Indiana and in lower Ohio River tributaries in southwestern Indiana. Common in appropriate habitats across its range. Listed as State Endangered in Illinois due to its limited range in that state.

INDIANA CRAYFISH
Orconectes indianensis (Hay 1896)

KEY CHARACTERS

1. Two short terminal elements on form I male gonopod that diverge from one another
2. Rostrum with weak median carina

SIMILAR SPECIES

- Shawnee Crayfish [*Orconectes illinoiensis*]
- Allegheny Crayfish [*O. obscurus*]
- Northern Clearwater Crayfish [*O. propinquus*]
- Sanborn's Crayfish [*O. sanbornii*]
- Little Wabash Crayfish [*O. stannardi*]

DESCRIPTION Rostrum excavated; straight or nearly straight margins that terminate in small spines, weakly developed carina present. Chela large with moderately long fingers, two rows of rounded turbercles along mesial margin of palm region. Areola wide. Form I male gonopod with two short divergent elements, elements form a distinct V when viewed from side. Life colors dark brown, tips of fingers red with black subterminal bands.

Differs from the Northern Clearwater, Allegheny, Shawnee, Sanborn's, and Little Wabash Crayfish by possessing a form I gonopod with strongly divergent terminal elements.

HABITAT Found in small- to medium-sized creeks with firm substrates of mud, gravel, or cobble. Usually found under rocks or in woody debris.

A   B   C   D

DISTRIBUTION & STATUS Found in a narrow karst region of south-central Indiana. The Unarmed Crayfish (*O. inermis testii*) occurs only caves in Monroe Co. while the Ghost Crayfish (*O. inermis inermis*) occurs in caves from Monroe Co. south to the Ohio River. Uncommon given the scarcity of its specialized habitat, generally occurs in low population sizes in caves. Listed as State Rare in Indiana.

GHOST/UNARMED CRAYFISH
Orconectes inermis inermis Cope 1872
Orconectes inermis testii Hay 1891

KEY CHARACTERS
1. Lack of pigment in small eyes and on body

SIMILAR SPECIES
None, should not be confused with any other midwestern species.

DESCRIPTION Eyes greatly reduced and lacking pigment. Rostrum excavated; straight or nearly straight margins that either terminate in small spines or tubercles (Ghost Crayfish) or terminate bluntly (Unarmed Crayfish). Chela thin with moderately long and thin fingers. Many sharp spines on hepatic regions of carapace. Areola wide. Form I male gonopod with two very short divergent elements. Life color white to light yellow, no pigmentation on fingers of chela. As true troglobitic organisms, both subspecies differ from all other midwestern crayfishes by lacking pigmentation in eyes and body and having long, spindly legs and chela.

HABITAT Subterranean creeks flowing through karst topography. Usually found in pools with silt and sand substrates.

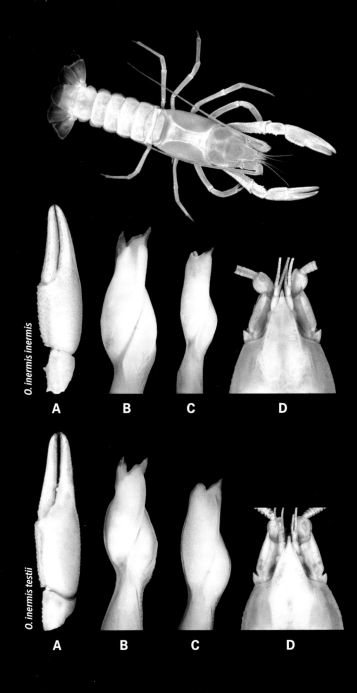

O. inermis inermis

A B C D

O. inermis testii

A B C D

DISTRIBUTION & STATUS Restricted to direct tributaries to the Ohio River in extreme southern Indiana. Common in its range.

KENTUCKY RIVER CRAYFISH
Orconectes juvenilis (Hagen 1870)

KEY CHARACTERS
1. Two long thin elements on form I male gonopod, both elongated, thin and mostly straight
2. Rostrum without median carina

SIMILAR SPECIES
- Spiny Stream Crayfish [*Orconectes cristavarius*]
- Golden Crayfish [*O. luteus*]
- Phallic Crayfish [*O. putnami*]
- Norwood River Crayfish [*O. raymondi*]
- Rusty Crayfish [*O. rusticus*]
- Sinkhole Crayfish [*O. theaphionensis*]

DESCRIPTION Rostrum moderately excavated, without carina; margins slightly curved, slightly converging, with terminal spines, acumen short. Mesial margin of palm of chela with two rows of tubercles. Areola moderately wide. Form I male gonopod with two elongated, mostly straight elements, tip of central project with slight arch and curved tip, strong angular shoulder present. Life colors olive green to a reddish brown, tips of fingers of chela red with black subterminal bands.

Differs from the Phallic and Spiny Stream Crayfish by having straight-edged mandibles; differs from Norwood River and Sinkhole Crayfish by lacking median carina on rostrum; differs from the Rusty Crayfish by having longer form I gonopod elements and lacking the rust-colored spot on posterior sides of the carapace; differs from Golden Crayfish by lacking two dark dorsal saddles.

HABITAT Occurs in small to large streams and rivers with mud, gravel, cobble, or boulder substrates. They are most commonly found under large gravel or rocks, but can occasionally be found in woody debris or undercut banks.

A   **B**   **C**   **D**

DISTRIBUTION & STATUS Restricted to Ohio River tributaries in extreme southeastern Illinois. Common in its range. Listed as State Endangered in Illinois due to its restricted range in that state.

KENTUCKY CRAYFISH
Orconectes kentuckiensis Rhoades 1944

KEY CHARACTERS
1. Two short terminal elements on form I male gonopod, central projection bladelike and slightly curved

SIMILAR SPECIES
- Sloan Crayfish [*Orconectes sloanii*]

DESCRIPTION Rostrum deeply excavated, without median carina; margins straight, slightly converging and terminating in spines. Chela large with moderately long fingers, fingers usually covered with short setae, two rows of well-developed tubercles along mesial margin of palm region. Areola moderately wide. Form I male gonopod without shoulder, two short curved elements, both elements diverge from one another and curve away from the ventral surface of the crayfish when gonopod is laying in normal position between bases of walking legs, central projection stout. Life colors light brown, body irregularly mottled, tips of fingers orange with black subterminal bands.

Differs from the Sloan Crayfish by possessing a central projection having less distinct subterminal notch and lacking a pronounced tip at distal end.

HABITAT Found in small to large streams, usually found under cobble or gravel in rocky pools or riffles.

A   B   C   D

DISTRIBUTION & STATUS Found only in the Gulf Coastal Plain of extreme southern Illinois. Uncommon in appropriate habitats in Illinois. Listed as State Endangered in Illinois because it is currently known from a single oxbow lake (Horseshoe Lake) in that state.

SHRIMP CRAYFISH
Orconectes lancifer (Hagen 1870)

KEY CHARACTERS
1. Rostrum with very long, sharply pointed acumen
2. Laterally compressed body with short areola
3. Small chela

SIMILAR SPECIES
None, should not be confused with any other midwestern species.

DESCRIPTION Rostrum excavated; straight margins that terminate in small spines, very long acumen. Chela long and narrow with short fingers, very weak turbercles along mesial margin of palm region. Areola closed or linear at its midpoint. Form I male gonopod with two short divergent elements with tips that slightly curve. Life colors a mottled pattern of reds, browns, or greens over a cream base color, tips of fingers light orange.

Differs from all other midwestern crayfishes by possessing a very long acumen, a closed areola, short fingers on thin chela, and a more laterally compressed carapace. Latter two characteristics responsible for the species' common name as the body appears more shrimplike than crayfishlike.

HABITAT Cypress swamps and other permanently flooded low areas near creeks or lakes. Usually found amongst dense growths of live aquatic vegetation.

DISTRIBUTION & STATUS Found in the Iowa and Des Moines river drainages in southern Minnesota and central Iowa and small direct tributaries of the Mississippi River in western Illinois and northeastern Missouri. Common in appropriate habitats across its range.

GOLDEN CRAYFISH
Orconectes luteus (Creaser 1933)

KEY CHARACTERS
1. Two dark saddle marks across top of carapace
2. Two long straight terminal elements on form I male gonopod

SIMILAR SPECIES
- Kentucky River Crayfish [*Orconectes juvenilis*]
- Leopard Crayfish [*O. pardalotus*]
- Bigclaw Crayfish [*O. placidus*]
- Rusty Crayfish [*O. rusticus*]

DESCRIPTION Rostrum excavated; straight or nearly straight margins that terminate in strong spines, well-developed carina present or absent. Chela large with moderately long fingers, two rows of rounded turbercles along mesial margin of palm region. Areola wide. Form I male gonopod with two long, thin, and straight elements, elements in line with main shaft, tip of central projection curved away from body when gonopod is laying in normal position between bases of walking legs. Life colors variable, base color light to olive green to yellow, two widely spaced dark brown or black saddles across top and sides of carapace, tips of fingers red, tips occasionally with black subterminal bands.

Differs from the Rusty Crayfish in possessing two dark saddles and lacking an angular shoulder on the form I gonopod and rusty colored spots on the lateral surfaces of the carapace; differs from Kentucky River Crayfish in possessing two dark saddles and slightly shorter terminal gonopod elements; differs from Bigclaw Crayfish by possessing a nearly straight-edged mandible, shorter fingers; differs from Leopard Crayfish by possessing a nearly straight-edged mandible and lacking dark, scattered spots across the body.

HABITAT Found in small, flowing creeks to large navigable rivers. Usually found under gravel or rocks in areas with permanent flow.

A   B   C   D

DISTRIBUTION & STATUS Found in Ohio River drainage in extreme eastern Ohio. Declining in streams in eastern Ohio that have been invaded by Rusty Crayfish. The species is still common in those streams not invaded by Rusty Crayfish.

ALLEGHENY CRAYFISH
Orconectes obscurus (Hagen 1870)

KEY CHARACTERS
1. Two short straight terminal elements, well-developed shoulder at the base of the central projection on form I male gonopod

SIMILAR SPECIES
- Shawnee Crayfish [*Orconectes illinoiensis*]
- Indiana Crayfish [*O. indianensis*]
- Northern Clearwater Crayfish [*O. propinquus*]
- Sanborn's Crayfish [*O. sanbornii*]
- Little Wabash Crayfish [*O. stannardi*]

DESCRIPTION Rostrum excavated; straight or nearly straight margins that terminate in strong spines. Chela large with moderately long fingers, two rows of rounded turbercles along mesial margin of palm region. Areola moderately wide. Form I male gonopod with two short straight elements, elements in line with main shaft and with nearly straight dorsal edge, well-developed shoulder at base of central projection. Life colors light brown, dark dorsal saddle usually present at rear of carapace, dark brown wedge on dorsal surface of abdomen; tips of fingers orange with black subterminal bands.

Differs from Northern Clearwater and Little Wabash Crayfish by lacking a median carina on its rostrum and having a well-developed shoulder at the base of the central projection on the form I gonopod; differs from Shawnee and Sanborn's Crayfish by possessing a strong shoulder at the base of the form I gonopod elements; differs from Indiana Crayfish by having very straight, non-divergent terminal elements of the form I gonopod.

HABITAT Found in small- to medium-sized creeks with firm substrates of sand, gravel, or cobble. Usually found under rocks or cobble, occasionally collected in woody debris.

DISTRIBUTION & STATUS Known only from the main channel of the Ohio River along the Illinois-Kentucky border. Given that large, deep rivers are difficult to sample, the species' current population status is unknown.

LEOPARD CRAYFISH
Orconectes pardalotus Wetzel, Poly, and Fetzner 2005

KEY CHARACTERS
1. Chela with long fingers, larger individuals with wide gap between bases of fingers
2. Terminal elements of gonopod long and thin
3. Body covered with dark spots or blotches

SIMILAR SPECIES
- Kentucky River Crayfish [*Orconectes juvenilis*]
- Golden Crayfish [*O. luteus*]
- Bigclaw Crayfish [*O. placidus*]
- Rusty Crayfish [*O. rusticus*]

DESCRIPTION Rostrum excavated; concave margins terminating in spines at base of long acumen, weak median carina occasionally present. Chela large, with long fingers, dactyl of chela greater than two times length of mesial margin of the palm. Areola wide. Form I male gonopod lacking angular shoulder at caudal base and terminating in two long, thin, and straight elements, elements in line with main shaft, tip of central projection curved away from body when gonopod is laying in normal position between bases of walking legs. Life color light tan to brown with dark spots or blotches covering carapace, abdomen, and chela.

Differs from all other midwestern crayfish with two long, thin terminal gonopod elements in having dark spots scattered over the body. Also differs from those species in the following respects: from Bigclaw Crayfish by lacking a large distomedian spine on the ventral surface of the carpus; from Golden Crayfish by lacking two dark dorsal saddles; from Rusty and Kentucky River Crayfish in having a dentate mandible.

HABITAT Large rivers. Usually found under gravel and rocks.

Specimen photo by James Wetzel.

A   B   C   D

DISTRIBUTION & STATUS Ohio River main stem and Big Creek drainage in extreme southeastern Illinois. Common in appropriate habitat across its limited range. Listed as State Endangered in Illinois due to its limited range in that state.

BIGCLAW CRAYFISH
Orconectes placidus (Hagen 1870)

KEY CHARACTERS
1. Chela with long fingers and dark spot at base of moveable finger
2. No shoulder on cephalic margin of form I gonopod
3. Terminal elements of gonopod long and thin
4. Weak median carina

SIMILAR SPECIES
- Kentucky River Crayfish [*Orconectes juvenilis*]
- Golden Crayfish [*O. luteus*]
- Leopard Crayfish [*O. pardalotus*]
- Rusty Crayfish [*O. rusticus*]

DESCRIPTION Rostrum excavated; nearly parallel margins terminating in spines at base of long acumen, carina occasionally present. Chela large, with long fingers, dactyl of chela greater than two times length of mesial margin of the palm. Areola moderately wide. Form I male gonopod lacking angular shoulder at caudal base and terminating in two long, thin, and straight elements, elements in line with main shaft; tip of central projection curved away from body when gonopod is laying in normal position between bases of walking legs. Life colors tan to olive green with two dark brown or black saddles occasionally present; dark spot at base of moveable finger.

Differs from the Rusty Crayfish in possessing two dark saddles and lacking an angular shoulder on the form I gonopod and rusty colored spots on the lateral surfaces of the carapace; differs from Kentucky River Crayfish in possessing two dark saddles and slightly shorter terminal gonopod elements; differs from Golden Crayfish in possessing a strongly dentate mandible and possessing a dark spot at the base of the moveable finger of the chela.

HABITAT Small- to medium-sized creeks and large rivers. Usually found under gravel and rocks in areas with permanent flow.

A   B   C   D

DISTRIBUTION & STATUS Mississippi River and Great Lakes drainages from eastern Minnesota and Iowa to northern Ohio, also in the Wabash River drainage of Illinois and Indiana. Widespread and abundant in appropriate habitats across the upper Midwest east of the Mississippi River.

NORTHERN CLEARWATER CRAYFISH

Orconectes propinquus (Girard 1852)

KEY CHARACTERS
1. Two short straight terminal elements on form I male gonopod
2. Strong median carina on rostrum

SIMILAR SPECIES
* Shawnee Crayfish
  [*Orconectes illinoiensis*]
* Indiana Crayfish
  [*O. indianensis*]
* Allegheny Crayfish
  [*O. obscurus*]
* Sanborn's Crayfish
  [*O. sanbornii*]
* Little Wabash Crayfish
  [*O. stannardi*]

DESCRIPTION Rostrum excavated; nearly straight or slightly concave margins that terminate in strong spines; strong median carina present. Chela large with moderately long fingers, two rows of rounded tubercles along mesial margin of palm region. Areola wide. Form I male gonopod with two short straight elements, elements in line with main shaft and with nearly straight dorsal edge. Life colors light tan to brown, dark brown tapering wedge on dorsal surface of abdomen, tips of fingers red or orange with black subterminal bands.

Differs from the Allegheny Crayfish by possessing a rostrum with a strong median carina and lacking a well-developed shoulder at the base of the central projection on the form I gonopod; differs from Little Wabash Crayfish in lacking a caudal spur on mesial process of the form I gonopod; differs from Shawnee and Sanborn's Crayfish by possessing a strong median carina; differs from Indiana Crayfish by having very straight, non-divergent terminal elements of the form I gonopod.

HABITAT Found in small creeks to medium-sized rivers with firm substrates of gravel or cobble. Usually found under rocks or cobble.

A   B   C   D

DISTRIBUTION & STATUS Lower portion of the Missouri River drainage in east-central Missouri. Common in appropriate habitats.

SPOTHANDED CRAYFISH
Orconectes punctimanus (Creaser 1933)

KEY CHARACTERS
1. Two long, slightly curved terminal elements on form I male gonopod
2. Large, sharp tubercles along mesial margin of chela
3. Dark spot at base of moveable finger

SIMILAR SPECIES
- Calico Crayfish [*Orconectes immunis*]
- Virile Crayfish [*O. virilis*]

DESCRIPTION Rostrum excavated; nearly straight converging margins that terminate in strong spines. Chela large with moderately long fingers; large, sharp tubercles along mesial margin of palm and moveable finger. Areola moderately wide. Form I male gonopod with two long thin elements, both elements slightly curve away from the ventral surface of the crayfish when gonopod is laying in its normal position between bases of walking legs. Life colors dark tan to reddish brown, small dark spot at base of moveable finger on chela; some darker mottling may be present on dorsal surface of carapace; tips of fingers orange.

Differs from the Virile Crayfish by lacking a pair of dark blotches on each abdominal segment, possessing a dark spot at the base of the moveable finger of the chela, and having longer form I gonopod elements (central projection usually greater than 45% of the total length of the gonopod vs. less than 45%); differs from the Calico Crayfish in having longer, slightly curved terminal elements on the form I gonopod and lacking a deep incision at the base of the moveable finger.

HABITAT Found in all sizes of creeks and rivers. Usually found in areas with slower flows and rooted vegetation; can also be found in woody debris piles and under larger rocks.

DISTRIBUTION & STATUS Restricted to a few direct tributaries to the Ohio River in extreme southern Indiana. Common in appropriate habitats in its range.

PHALLIC CRAYFISH
Orconectes putnami (Faxon 1884)

KEY CHARACTERS
1. Rostrum without median carina
2. Two very long and thin elements on form I male gonopod

SIMILAR SPECIES
- Spiny Stream Crayfish [*Orconectes cristavarius*]
- Kentucky River Crayfish [*O. juvenilis*]
- Golden Crayfish [*O. luteus*]
- Norwood River Crayfish [*O. raymondi*]
- Rusty Crayfish [*O. rusticus*]
- Sinkhole Crayfish [*O. theaphionensis*]

DESCRIPTION Rostrum moderately excavated, without carina; margins nearly straight, gradually converging, with terminal spines, acumen long. Chela large with moderately long fingers, mesial margin of palm of chela with two rows of tubercles. Areola moderately wide. Form I male gonopod with two very long, thin, mostly straight elements, tip of central project with slight arch and curved tip, angular shoulder at base of central projection. Life colors light brown to olive green, tips of fingers of chela with black band and terminal red band, large knobs on palm of chela yellow to bright orange; faint tapering wedge on dorsal surface of abdomen.

Differs from all other midwestern crayfishes in having very long terminal elements on form I gonopod (>50% of total length of gonopod). Other differences as follows: differs from Rusty and Kentucky River Crayfish by having a dentate mandibles; differs from Norwood River, Spiny Stream Crayfish, and Sinkhole Crayfish by lacking median carina on rostrum; differs from Golden Crayfish by lacking two dark dorsal saddles.

HABITAT Occurs in small to large streams and rivers with mud, gravel, cobble, or boulder substrates. They are most commonly found under large gravel or rocks, but can occasionally be found in woody debris or undercut banks.

A   B   C   D

DISTRIBUTION & STATUS Currently known only from Ohio River tributaries in extreme southwestern Ohio (Brown and Adams counties). Common in appropriate habitat across its limited range.

NORWOOD RIVER CRAYFISH
Orconectes raymondi Thoma and Stocker 2009

KEY CHARACTERS

1. Two long thin elements on form I male gonopod, both elongated and mostly straight
2. Median carina

SIMILAR SPECIES

- Spiny Stream Crayfish [*Orconectes cristavarius*]
- Kentucky River Crayfish [*O. juvenilis*]
- Golden Crayfish [*O. luteus*]
- Phallic Crayfish [*O. putnami*]
- Rusty Crayfish [*O. rusticus*]
- Sinkhole Crayfish [*O. theaphionensis*]

DESCRIPTION Rostrum deeply excavated, with strong median carina; margins curved and concave in appearance, slightly converging and terminating in spines. Chela large with moderately long fingers, two to four loosely organized rows of well-developed tubercles along mesial margin of palm region. Areola moderately wide. Form I male gonopod with two long, thin elements, angular shoulder at base of central projection, tip of central projection slightly curves away from the ventral surface of the crayfish when gonopod is laying in normal position between bases of walking legs. Life colors brown to greenish-brown, tips of fingers red to orange with black subterminal bands.

Differs from the Rusty, Phallic, and Kentucky River Crayfish by possessing a median carina; differs from Golden Crayfish in having tubercles in mesial palm region not restricted to two well-defined rows; differs from Sinkhole Crayfish by possessing a central projection with a curved tip; differs from Spiny Stream Crayfish by having a straight-edged mandible.

HABITAT Small- to medium-sized creeks. Usually found under gravel and rocks in areas with permanent flow.

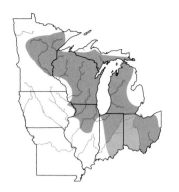

DISTRIBUTION & STATUS Native to Ohio River and Great Lakes drainages northeast Michigan, western Ohio, and eastern and central Indiana. Widely introduced across the Midwest (shown in orange). Widespread and abundant. Rapidly expanding due to introductions throughout the Midwest where it is displacing native species.

RUSTY CRAYFISH
Orconectes rusticus (Girard 1852)

KEY CHARACTERS
1. Prominent rust colored spot on side of carapace
2. Terminal elements of gonopod moderately long and thin

SIMILAR SPECIES
- Spiny Stream Crayfish [*Orconectes cristavarius*]
- Kentucky River Crayfish [*O. juvenilis*]
- Golden Crayfish [*O. luteus*]
- Phallic Crayfish [*O. putnami*]
- Norwood River Crayfish [*O. raymondi*]
- Sinkhole Crayfish [*O. theaphionensis*]

DESCRIPTION Rostrum deeply excavated, median carina absent; margins curved and concave in appearance, slightly converging and terminating in spines. Chela large, with moderately long fingers. Areola moderately wide. Form I male gonopod with strong angular shoulder at base of central projection, terminating in two moderately long, straight, and thin elements. Life colors olive green to rust with large rusty or brown colored spot on posterior-lateral surfaces of carapace, tips of finger orange with wide black subterminal bands.

Differs from all other midwestern species by possessing rust colored spots on the sides of the carapace. Also differs from other similar species in the following respects: differs from the Phallic and Spiny Stream Crayfish by having straight-edged mandibles; differs from Norwood and Sinkhole Crayfish by lacking median carina on rostrum; differs from the Kentucky River Crayfish by having shorter form I gonopods; differs from Golden Crayfish by lacking two dark dorsal saddles.

HABITAT Can be found in rivers, reservoirs, and creeks of all sizes with most substrates including riprap, cobble, wood debris, submerged logs, and vegetation.

A B C D

DISTRIBUTION & STATUS Widespread throughout a wide north-south band in Ohio from Lake Erie to the Ohio River. Common in its range.

SANBORN'S CRAYFISH
Orconectes sanbornii (Faxon 1884)

KEY CHARACTERS
1. Rostrum without median carina
2. Two short straight elements on form I male gonopod

SIMILAR SPECIES
- Shawnee Crayfish [*Orconectes illinoiensis*]
- Indiana Crayfish [*O. indianensis*]
- Allegheny Crayfish [*O. obscurus*]
- Northern Clearwater Crayfish [*O. propinquus*]
- Little Wabash Crayfish [*O. stannardi*]

DESCRIPTION Rostrum moderately excavated; straight, slightly converging margins, with terminal spines, acumen long. Chela large with moderately long fingers, palm of chela with two rows of tubercles. Areola moderately wide. Form I male gonopod without shoulder, two short, stout, straight parallel elements. Life colors light brown to tan, chela much lighter in color, dark brown tapering wedge on dorsal surface of abdomen, tips of fingers of chela red or orange.

Differs from the Allegheny Crayfish by lacking a large shoulder on the form I gonopod; differs from the Northern Clearwater Crayfish by lacking a carina on rostrum; differs from Little Wabash Crayfish in lacking a caudal spur on mesial process of the form I gonopod; differs from Shawnee Crayfish in having straight rostral margins; differs from Indiana Crayfish by having very straight, non-divergent terminal elements of the form I gonopod.

HABITAT Usually found in small- to medium-sized creeks with gravel and cobble substrates, but can be found along edges of large rivers. They are most commonly encountered under large gravel or rocks.

A   B   C   D

DISTRIBUTION & STATUS Found in Ohio River drainage of southeastern Indiana and extreme southwestern Ohio. Common in its range.

SLOAN CRAYFISH
Orconectes sloanii (Bundy 1876)

KEY CHARACTERS
1. Two short terminal elements on form I male gonopod, central projection bladelike and slightly curved

SIMILAR SPECIES
• Kentucky Crayfish [*Orconectes kentuckiensis*]

DESCRIPTION Rostrum deeply excavated, with weak carina; margins nearly straight, slightly converging and terminating in spines, acumen long. Palm of chela with two rows of rounded tubercles. Areola wide. Form I male gonopod without shoulder, two short slightly curved elements, both elements diverge from one another and curve away from the ventral surface of the crayfish when gonopod is laying in normal position between bases of walking legs, central projection gradually tapering to tip. Life colors light brown, dark dorsal saddle on posterior edge of carapace, tips of fingers orange with black subterminal bands.

Differs from Kentucky Crayfish by possessing a central projection on the form I gonopod that gradually tapers to a thin tip.

HABITAT Occurs in small to large streams, where it is mostly found under cobble or gravel.

A   B   C   D

DISTRIBUTION & STATUS Found only in the Little Wabash River drainage in southeastern Illinois. Common in appropriate habitats across its range in southeastern Illinois.

LITTLE WABASH CRAYFISH
Orconectes stannardi Page 1985

KEY CHARACTERS
1. Two short straight terminal elements on form I male gonopod with spur on mesial process
2. Rostrum with median carina

SIMILAR SPECIES
- Shawnee Crayfish [*Orconectes illinoiensis*]
- Indiana Crayfish [*O. indianensis*]
- Allegheny Crayfish [*O. obscurus*]
- Northern Clearwater Crayfish [*O. propinquus*]
- Sanborn's Crayfish [*O. sanbornii*]

DESCRIPTION Rostrum excavated; straight or nearly straight margins that terminate in strong spines, well-developed carina present. Chela large with moderately long fingers, two rows of rounded turbercles along mesial margin of palm region. Areola wide. Form I male gonopod with two short straight elements, elements in line with main shaft; mesial process with short spur or projection that angles away from the ventral surface of the crayfish when gonopod is laying in normal position between bases of walking legs. Life colors light to olive brown, tips of fingers red with black subterminal bands.

Differs from the Northern Clearwater, Allegheny, Sanborn's, and Shawnee Crayfish in possessing a spur on mesial process of form I gonopod; differs from Indiana Crayfish by having very straight terminal elements of the form I gonopod.

HABITAT Found in small- to medium-sized creeks with firm substrates of mud, gravel, or cobble. Usually found under rocks or in woody debris.

A B C D

DISTRIBUTION & STATUS Currently known only from a limited portion of the East Fork White River drainage in south-central Indiana (Lost River and Blue Creek drainages). Common in appropriate habitat across its limited range.

SINKHOLE CRAYFISH
Orconectes theaphionensis Simon, Timm, and Morris 2005

KEY CHARACTERS
1. Two long, thin and straight terminal elements of form I gonopod
2. Median carina

SIMILAR SPECIES
- Spiny Stream Crayfish [*Orconectes cristavarius*]
- Kentucky River Crayfish [*O. juvenilis*]
- Golden Crayfish [*O. luteus*]
- Phallic Crayfish [*O. putnami*]
- Norwood River Crayfish [*O. raymondi*]
- Rusty Crayfish [*O. rusticus*]

DESCRIPTION Rostrum deeply excavated, with strong median carina; margins nearly straight, slightly converging and terminating in spines, acumen long. Chela large with moderately long fingers; two rows of well-developed tubercles along mesial margin of palm region. Areola moderately wide. Form I male gonopod with two long, thin elements, angular shoulder at base of central projection, tip of central projection straight. Life colors light brown to olive green, dark dorsal saddle at posterior edge of carapace, faint tapering wedge on dorsal surface of abdomen, tips of fingers red to orange with black subterminal bands.

Differs from the Rusty, Phallic, and Kentucky River Crayfish by possessing a median carina; differs from Golden and Norwood River Crayfish in possessing a form I central projection with a straight tip; differs from Spiny Stream Crayfish in having a straight-edged mandible.

HABITAT Small- to large-sized creeks with substrates of bedrock, boulders, cobble, or large gravel. Usually found under gravel and rocks in areas with flow.

A   B   C   D

DISTRIBUTION & STATUS Found across the Midwest with the exception of southern Indiana, southeastern Michigan, and most of Ohio. It is the most widely distributed crayfish in North America and has also been introduced across other regions of Ohio and the continent. Widespread and abundant across the Midwest.

VIRILE CRAYFISH
Orconectes virilis (Hagen 1870)

KEY CHARACTERS
1. Two long, slightly curved terminal elements on form I male gonopod
2. Large, sharp tubercles along mesial margin of chela
3. Paired dark angled blotches on abdominal segments

SIMILAR SPECIES
- Calico Crayfish [*Orconectes immunis*]
- Spothanded Crayfish [*O. punctimanus*]

DESCRIPTION Rostrum excavated; nearly straight converging margins that terminate in strong spines. Chela large with moderately long fingers; large, sharp tubercles along mesial margin of palm and moveable finger, tubercles usually angled forward. Areola narrowly open. Form I male gonopod with two long thin elements, both elements slightly curve away from the ventral surface of the crayfish when gonopod is laying in normal position between bases of walking legs. Life colors light brown to greenish brown; tips of fingers orange; pair of dark angled blotches on each abdominal segment; some darker mottling may be present on dorsal surface of carapace.

Differs from the Spothanded Crayfish by possessing a pair of dark angled blotches on each abdominal segment, lacking a dark spot at the base of the moveable finger of the chela, and having shorter form I gonopod elements (central projection usually less than 45% of the total length of the gonopod vs. greater than 45%); differs from Calico Crayfish in having longer, slightly curved terminal elements on the form I gonopod and lacking a deep incision at the base of the moveable finger.

HABITAT Found in all types of permanent aquatic habitats, from small creeks to the Great Lakes, with substrates and cover of all types. Usually more common in areas with slower flows in creeks and rivers.

A   B   C   D

DISTRIBUTION & STATUS Mississippi River and Great Lakes drainages across eastern Iowa and Missouri, all of Illinois, eastern and southern Wisconsin, and northern and central Indiana and Ohio. The species is frequently used in the bait trade so other isolated and undocumented populations in the Midwest may exist. Widespread and common across its range.

WHITE RIVER CRAWFISH
Procambarus acutus (Girard 1852)

KEY CHARACTERS
1. Red coloration in large adults; open areola
2. Four short, curved terminal elements on form I male gonopod
3. Carapace covered with small tubercles

SIMILAR SPECIES
- Red Swamp Crawfish [*Procambarus clarkii*]

DESCRIPTION Rostrum flat; margins converge terminally and terminate in small spines at the base of a short acumen. Chela long and thin with dorsal surfaces covered with small tubercles. Areola narrowly open. Carapace covered with small tubercles. Form I male gonopod with four short terminal elements that curve lateral to the main shaft of the gonopod. Elements frequently obscured by setae. Life colors of large adults brick red with a dark, tapering black wedge on dorsal surface of the abdomen. Color of smaller adults and juveniles light brown or tan and frequently speckled with small dark spots.

Differs from Red Swamp Crawfish in having an open areola.

HABITAT Found in a wide variety of habitats, from lakes to lowland swamps to medium-sized creeks and rivers. Usually not present in habitats with strong flow.

DISTRIBUTION & STATUS Found natively only in Mississippi and Ohio river drainages in extreme southern Illinois. Several introduced and widely scattered populations are known from across the Midwest. The species is frequently used in the bait, pet, and aquaculture trades and is one of the most widely introduced crayfish species in the world. Other isolated and undocumented populations in the Midwest may exist. Common in appropriate habitats in its native southern Illinois range.

RED SWAMP CRAWFISH
Procambarus clarkii (Girard 1852)

KEY CHARACTERS
1. Red coloration in large adults
2. Closed areola
3. Four short terminal elements on form I male gonopod
4. Carapace covered with small tubercles

SIMILAR SPECIES
- White River Crawfish [*Procambarus acutus*]

DESCRIPTION Rostrum flat; margins converge terminally and terminate in small spines at the base of a short acumen. Chela long and thin with dorsal surfaces covered with small tubercles. Areola closed or linear at its midpoint. Carapace covered with small tubercles. Form I male gonopod with four short terminal elements that curve away from the ventral surface of the crayfish when gonopod is laying in its normal position between bases of walking legs. Elements frequently obscured by setae. Large, angular shoulder on caudal edge of gonopod. Life colors of large adults brick red with a dark, tapering black wedge on dorsal surface of abdomen. Color of smaller adults and juveniles light brown or tan and frequently speckled with small dark spots.

Differs from White River Crawfish in that its areola is closed.

HABITAT Found in its native range in swamps, vegetated ponds, and flooded lowland ditches. Introduced populations of the species occur in ponds and lakes of all types and slow flowing creeks.

A B C D

DISTRIBUTION & STATUS Mississippi and Wabash river drainages from central Iowa and Missouri to extreme western Indiana. Also in the Lake Michigan drainage of southeastern Wisconsin and northeastern Illinois. Difficult to assess status due to the species' burrowing behavior, but there is currently no evidence of recent population declines across its range. The massive loss of habitat during the conversion of prairie to agricultural lands in the Midwest has surely resulted in population declines during the 1800s and early 1900s.

PRAIRIE CRAYFISH
Procambarus gracilis (Bundy 1876)

KEY CHARACTERS
1. Closed areola
2. Four short, curved terminal elements on form I male gonopod
3. Large, angular tubercles along mesial margin of palm of chela

SIMILAR SPECIES
- Devil Crayfish [*Cambarus diogenes*]
- Paintedhand Mudbug [*C. polychromatus*]
- Little Brown Mudbug [*C. thomai*]
- Digger Crayfish [*Fallicambarus fodiens*]

DESCRIPTION Rostrum wide at its base and excavated; margins converge terminally and merge with base of short acumen, terminal marginal spines not present. Chela wide and triangular in shape, with large, forward angling tubercles along mesial margin of palm region. Areola closed or linear at its midpoint. Form I male gonopod with four short terminal elements, two of which are noticeably thinner than other elements. Life colors generally dark to reddish brown. Large adults can be bright red or orange.

Differs from all other midwestern crayfish with closed areolas by having pronounced tubercles along the mesial margin of the palm and having four short terminal elements on the form I gonopod.

HABITAT A primary burrowing species, the Prairie Crayfish is found in burrows up to several feet deep. Populations are normally found in grasslands and fields that were formerly wet prairies and in ephemerally flooded woodlands near bogs. Adults can be encountered in ephemeral ponds and small sluggish flowing streams during the spring.

A   B   C   D

DISTRIBUTION & STATUS Found only in the Mississippi and Ohio river drainages in extreme southern Illinois. Common in appropriate habitats in its range.

VERNAL CRAYFISH
Procambarus viaeviridis (Faxon 1914)

KEY CHARACTERS
1. Open areola
2. Four short, curved terminal elements on form I male gonopod
3. Smooth rostral margins

SIMILAR SPECIES
• White River Crawfish [*Procambarus acutus*]

DESCRIPTION Rostrum flat; curved margins that converge terminally and merge with base of a short acumen, terminal marginal spines not present. Chela thin, with large, forward angling tubercles along mesial margin of palm region. Areola narrowly open. Form I male gonopod with four short terminal elements. Elements frequently obscured by setae. Life colors light pink, reddish brown, or light brown with a dark, tapering black wedge on dorsal surface of abdomen.

Differs from White River Crawfish by lacking a red or speckled coloration and having smooth rostral margins.

HABITAT Found in cypress swamps and floodplains of small creeks and roadside ditches. Individuals inhabiting ephemerally flooded habitats will build burrows during dry periods.

A B C D

PART III

ADDITIONAL INFORMATION

GLOSSARY

ACUMEN   the pointed terminal extension of the rostrum.

ANNULUS VENTRALIS   the pocketlike structure with an elevated opening found on the underside of the female carapace; used for the storage of sperm.

ANTENNAL SCALE   the bladelike structure terminating in a spine found at the base of the antenna.

AREOLA   an area on the dorsal surface of the carapace located behind the cervical groove and forward of the abdomen and defined by a pair of shallow, gradually arching grooves.

CARAPACE   the hardened, unsegmented covering of the head and thoracic sections of the crayfish body.

CAUDAL PROCESS   one of the terminal elements of the gonopod, usually found on members of genera *Procambarus* and *Cambarellus*.

CENTRAL PROJECTION   one of the terminal elements of the gonopod, usually the largest. The central projection is corneous in the form I state.

CEPHALIC PROCESS   one of the terminal elements of the gonopod, found only on members of the genus *Procambarus*.

CERVICAL GROOVE   the transverse, shallow groove on the carapace that roughly separates the head region from the thoracic region.

CERVICAL SPINE   the sharp spine occurring on the cervical groove on the lateral surface of the carapace.

CHELA (CHELAE, PL.)   the enlarged clawlike terminal end of the first segment of the walking leg.

CORNEOUS   sclerotized, amber-colored. In reference to the appearance of certain terminal elements of the form I gonopod.

DACTYL   the movable, inner "finger" of the chela.

GONOPOD   the first pleopod of the male crayfish modified for sperm transfer.

ISCHIUM   the third most basal segment of the walking leg.

MEDIAN CARINA   a longitudinal elevated ridge found in the center of the floor of the rostrum.

MESIAL PROCESS   one of the terminal elements of the gonopod that is usually smaller than the central projection and noncorneous in the form I state.

PALM   the region of the chela running from the base of the dactyl to the base of the chela.

PEREIOPOD   the jointed walking leg of a crayfish. Crayfish have five pairs of pereiopods, the first of which is greatly enlarged and is known as the chela.

PLEOPOD   the jointed appendage found on the ventral surface of each abdominal segment. Crayfish have five pairs of pleopods. See also *gonopod*.

PROPODUS   the immovable outer "finger" of the chela.

PUNCTATION   a small, shallow, usually circular depression found on the external surface of the exoskeleton.

ROSTRUM   the triangular or rectangular-shaped dorsal extension of the carapace located between the eyes.

SHOULDER   a protruding, angular or rounded bulge found on the caudal surface of the gonopod, usually at the base of the central projection.

SPINE   a sharply pointed and elevated protrusion found on the surface of the exoskeleton.

SUBORBITAL ANGLE   the angle formed by a subsection of the anterior edge of the carapace just below the eye.

SUBPALMAR   the region at the base of the dactyl on the ventral, or underside, of the chela.

TUBERCLE   a hard, rounded and slightly elevated bump found on the surface of the exoskeleton.

LITERATURE CITED

Butler, R. S., R. J. DiStefano, and G. A. Schuster. 2003. Crayfish: an overlooked fauna. Endangered Species Bulletin 28(2):10–11.

Creaser, E. P. 1931. The Michigan decapod crustaceans. Papers of the Michigan Academy of Sciences Arts and Letters 13:257–276.

Helgen, J. C. 1990. The distribution of crayfishes (Decapoda, Cambaridae) in Minnesota. Report to Minnesota Department of Natural Resources, St. Paul.

Hobbs, H. H., Jr. 1981. The crayfishes of Georgia. Smithsonian Contributions of Zoology 318.

Hobbs, H. H., Jr. 1972. Crayfishes (Astacidae) of north and middle America. Biota of Freshwater Ecosystems, Identification Manual No. 9. United States Environmental Protection Agency, Washington, D. C.

Hobbs, H. H., III, and J. P. Jass. 1988. The crayfishes of Wisconsin. Milwaukee Public Museum, Special Publications in Biology and Geology No. 5.

Holthuis, L. B. 1952. A general revision of the Palaemonidae (Crustacea Decapoda Natantia) of the Americas, II. The subfamily Palaemoninae. Allan Hancock Foundation Occasional Paper 12.

Lodge, D. M., C. A. Taylor, D. M. Holdich, and J. Skudal. 2000. Nonindigenous crayfishes threaten North American freshwater biodiversity: lessons from Europe. Fisheries 25(8):7–20.

Momot, W. T. 1995. Redefining the role of crayfish in aquatic ecosystems. Reviews in Fisheries Science 3:33–63.

Page, L. M. 1985. The crayfishes and shrimps of Illinois. Illinois Natural History Survey Bulletin 33:335–448.

Pflieger, W. L. 1996. The crayfishes of Missouri. Missouri Department of Conservation, Jefferson City.

Taylor, C. A., G. A. Schuster, J. E. Cooper, R. J. DiStefano, A. G. Eversole, P. Hamr, H. H. Hobbs, III, H. W. Robison, C. E. Skelton, and R. F. Thoma. 2007. Conservation status of crayfishes of the United States and Canada after 10+ years of increased awareness. Fisheries 32 (8):372–389.

Thoma, R. F., and B. J. Armitage. 2008. Burrowing crayfish of Indiana. Final Report to Indiana Department of Natural Resources, Indianapolis.

Thoma, R. F., and R. F. Jezerinac. 2000. Ohio crayfish and shrimp atlas. Ohio Biological Survey Miscellaneous Contributions No. 7.

Thoma, R. H., and G. W. Stocker. 2009. *Orconectes* (*Procericambarus*) *raymondi* (Decapoda: Cambaridae), a new species of crayfish from southern Ohio. Proceedings of the Biological Society of Washington 122(4):405–413.

Wetzel, J. E. 2002. Form alteration of adult female crayfishes of the genus *Orconectes* (Decapoda: Cambaridae). American Midland Naturalist 147:326–337.

INDEX

ILLINOIS NATURAL HISTORY SURVEY MANUAL LIST

Illinois Natural History Survey Manuals, (includes field guides, field books, and field manuals), have been published at irregular intervals since 1936. These manuals are field guides that provide detailed descriptions and illustrations of a particular group of organisms (e.g., mammals, butterflies, reptiles and amphibians, freshwater mussels, etc.). INHS Manuals should fit into a jacket or coat pocket when used in the field. They offer complete species descriptions, including natural history, distribution, and status. Nature lovers, ranging from professional scientists to school children, can make use of these books.

OUT OF PRINT:

Manual 1: Fieldbook of Illinois Wildflowers (1936)
Manual 2: Fieldbook of Illinois Land Snails (1939)
Manual 3: Fieldbook of Illinois Shrubs (1942)
Manual 4: Fieldbook of Illinois Mammals (1957)
Manual 9: Field Guide to the Butterflies of Illinois (2001)

IN PRINT:

Manual 5: Field Guide to Freshwater Mussels of the Midwest (1992)
Manual 6: Field Guide to Northeastern Longhorned Beetles (1996)
Manual 7: Waterfowl of Illinois: An Abbreviated Field Guide (1999)
Manual 8: Field Guide to Amphibians and Reptiles of Illinois (1999)
Manual 10: Field Guide to the Silk Moths of Illinois (2002)
Manual 11: Field Guide to the Skipper Butterflies of Illinois 2nd Ed. (2010)
Manual 12: Field Manual of Illinois Mammals (2008)
Manual 13: Field Guide to the Sphinx Moths of Illinois (2010)
Manual 14: Butterflies of Illinois: A Field Guide (2014)
Manual 15: Field Guide to Crayfishes of the Midwest (2015)